CW00542886

Rosalka:

The Silkie Woman

and other stories, plays and poetry

Isobel Lodge

The Scottish Arts Club Charitable Trust, 2018

© Scottish Arts Club Charitable Trust – Isobel Lodge Award
All rights reserved
September 2018

The Isobel Lodge Award

Revenue from the sale of this collection of short stories, poetry and plays supports the annual £500 Isobel Lodge Award, open to unpublished writers born, living or studying in Scotland who enter the Scottish Arts Club Short Story Competition.

More information at www.storyawards.org

ISBN 978-1-9164667-3-9

Scottish Arts Club Charitable Trust
Scottish charity number SC044753
Registered Office:
24 Rutland Square,
Edinburgh
EH1 2BW
United Kingdom

Contents

"There is no greater agony than bearing an untold story inside you."

Maya Angelou, *I Know Why the Caged Bird Sings*

Dedicated to all unpublished writers, in whom the fire burns…

About Isobel Lodge

Isobel Lodge (1947-2016) was born in Thurso on the far north-east coast of Scotland. She was schooled at Hamilton and Forres Academies and took a degree at Aberdeen University, where she studied History, English, Greek and Moral Philosophy. At Southport she studied children's theatre, and she would bring her talents as an actress and a writer/director to many drama clubs for children and to local Christmas pantomimes in Edinburgh. Isobel wrote and directed with great charm, humour and invention, and often also starred. She was charismatic, larger than life, never happier than when performing, and wholly unafraid to sing, dance, and to appear as a bird, a plant, a man, the wicked Snow Queen, or the virtuous Betty Bee II.

She worked as a social worker in Edinburgh for 30 years where she used her talents as a storyteller to help neglected and abused children understand the processes they were going through and to feel confident enough to share their stories with others. In her free time, she loved to go out, to the theatre, the cinema, the Book Festival, concerts, the opera, art exhibitions, lectures and the ballet. It would be difficult to find anyone as passionate about the arts as she was and as open to their multiple forms and experiences. She was not so much a culture vulture as a culture swan; the arts were her element and she swam in them, drank them in, was inseparable from them.

In childhood she had filled the draughty old manses where she lived with stories of her own invention. In retirement, she took up the pen again and began writing short stories and poetry; she became an active member of the Scottish Arts Club and joined its writers' group. She was particularly gifted in atmospheric, descriptive scene-setting and in writing pithy dialogue. Tragically, just as she was gaining confidence in her abilities and writing more

1

often, she suffered the kind of sudden and dramatic ending that cannot be rewritten. Her family and friends set up a memorial fund in her honour to champion new Scottish writing with an annual short story award. It is a fitting tribute to a vibrant, creative woman who had several hundred friends and who, through the award that bears her name, continues to befriend, to encourage, and support new writing talent.

Rosalka: The Silkie Woman

Based on a fairy tale

She came from a seascape: Salt-kissed; surrounded by grey fragments of ancient rock; a forgotten place. The people were tough in that village, like the stalks of the heather on the hill. When you walk among the plants, they spring back at you, whipping your ankles. She woke to the hissing and howling of the wind and the forlorn cries of the sea-birds and she was rocked to sleep by the wind's hum and thrum, the drone and fall and the slap, slap, slapping of the waves. A gale held no fear for her. It was her lullaby. She was a wild thing, that child of the sea. I looked into her eyes and saw the ocean, grey green depths and brown flecks as the waves crashed into the pools. I knew I could drown in those eyes.

I was already an old man when I found that place. I was seeking solace somewhere remote. I thought the peace would help me compose. I rented a cottage apart from the others, overlooking the next bay and I had my piano transported with some difficulty along the single-track road. I thought I would just spend one spring and summer then migrate back to the city. Below me, crouching on the turf almost on the sand was another low, stone building with a corrugated iron roof. I could smell the acid from the peat smoke emerging from the chimney and saw that there was a crude washing line between two poles on the other side of the house, from which a pair of jeans and a tee shirt were flags in the wind. Also, a strange assortment of green straggling things seemed to be growing.

I first saw her when I was taking a walk on the rocks. The sun was bright, and the sea campion made splashes of pink on the sparkling granite. The air smelled of seaweed and the tunes of the waves in sea shells were playing in my head. I began to feel inspired again.

Suddenly, there she was in front of me, as if she had risen from a hidden rock pool. She was a strange unexpected creature, and yet she was of that place. She wore a green garment which appeared a mossy mass of threads and woven wool dangling in a darker hue in waves around her body. It would not have been out of place in a stage wardrobe except that it was rimed with salt and blackened by wet. I think she had green leggings underneath. Her auburn hair was tangled in tails dragging across her face and, though she had slime on her cheeks where she must have placed her fingers, I could see her bones were delicate and her skin pale and beautiful. At her feet was a pail full of black and green seaweed. She had that tight trapped-animal look.

I said a gentle "Hello", introduced myself as an itinerant composer here for the summer season, seeking quiet. She must be a neighbour? I asked. Her face opened a little, but she said nothing. Eventually, she pointed a dirty finger back in the direction of the beach. When I asked if I could help her with whatever task she was undertaking, she shook her head. She picked up the bucket and, unbidden, I followed her. I could hear the grunting of the seals on the point and the high calls of the gulls above, and the notes formed into a melody which I must have started to hum. She stopped, gestured to me to continue and began to hit a perfect rhythm on her pail. We must have formed an odd procession back to our beach. She never spoke a word and, when we reached her house, she turned away. Only when I was halfway up the path, and turned back to look, I saw her standing and she raised one hand in what might have been a salute of farewell.

I wouldn't see her for days and then I would find her gathering her crop from the sea, and we would fall into a companionable walk. She had no words. I did not know sign language, only music. Once she wrote on the sand, 'I cannot speak'. I told her I had words for both of us.

She seemed fragile, lonely. At last, she beckoned me into her

cottage. She would never come to mine and, when asked, would give her head a vigorous shake. We drank her brew of herbs and whisky in her kitchen while the sleety rain battered on the windows. Every surface was festooned with her artistic creations, weird clothes of shaggy green, dull brown and black, dolls and sculptures. She knitted and spun seaweed into magical shapes and fabrics. Pinned to cupboards, dresser and doors, were her poems, lyrical, unbearably sad. Her beauty disturbed me. I found my flesh rising and desiring. I wanted to touch her, but I did not dare. Once, when the door to the other room was open and she had gone out to the toilet, I looked inside. I saw above the bed a photo of a young man with fine aristocratic features framed with prayer flags of seaweed clothes, like a shrine. I knew thereafter that she was untouchable.

I have never frequented pubs, eschewing the noise and smell of stale alcohol, but I found after a time I craved some social interaction and I was curious. The only points of social contact in the village were the post office cum everything, manned by members of the community which was only open half a day, and the Fishers' Inn by the harbour which always appeared to be open. I took myself to the rather dark interior of the latter with its chipped tables and stools, bashed-about cushions and walls encrusted with glass-cased fish.

There was only one rather sodden local in a corner, falling asleep over his dram, so I was forced to engage with the barman/owner in a conversation which he initiated.

"You arr not from these pairts, arr you?"

In such a small community, of course, everybody knew everything, so he would probably have known my provenance even before my arrival. We conducted the usual dance of acquaintanceship which allowed me to enquire about my neighbour in casual tones.

"Och her, that would be Rosalka. A daft name if you ask me, and she's as daft as her name. I think she smokes that whacky backy.

She makes those weird things, sends them to London, makes a wee packet. Well, enough to get by. Those London folk are daft as well. They say her faither found her from the ocean – adopted she was. He was in the Merchant Navy, see, so he was always travelling. 'Found her' was probably just a way of saying it, if you take my meaning, but her mither was fair delighted with her 'wee fairy princess', she used to call her. She was such a bright one, always chattering, singing and dancing on the seashore. Aye you wouldn't believe... ." The man was garrulous when he started.

"But she is mute now?" I protested.

"Maybe a result of what happened."

"What?" I asked.

"Well first, her mither died of that cancer of the throat. Rosalka never wanted to go away from this place, leave the sea and go to the city, but her faither was keen. The Secondary said she had a talent. She had probably been seeing the young man for many summers before that. They were seen running on the dunes, wild as hares and well, you know, when the flesh is young? A young devil, the son and heir. That family only come to the Big Hoose in the summer, you see.

"Well Sandy, her faither, was anxious to get her away to the art college and another life. She went, but then Sandy had a heart attack and died. She came back. But, here's the strange thing, when she came back she couldn't speak."

"So, you think it was a result of all the loss she suffered?"

"Well Janie Gordon's daughter, Donella, was at the University at the same time and they were friends, so we heard some things. The young devil was at the same art college. The two were always together and Rosalka was so happy, she said she might even be able to settle in the city away from the sea if she could be with him for ever. He made promises, I believe." He leaned across the bar in a conspiratorial manner. "She may even have been pregnant for a while, but we don't really know. Anyway, he had an eye for anither, and she found out. Then she had a breakdown and, after a while in hospital, she came back here."

"Where is he now?"

"Och, I heard he went to work in London after his degree. The family don't often come in the summer anymore."

I seldom bought newspapers, but a few days after this conversation I did go to the shop to purchase a few groceries. I entered the shop to a buzz of conversation. Mrs McDougall behind the counter told me that as stranger I might not be interested, but the son of the Big Hoose was all over the papers – aristocracy after all – and he had married the daughter of a leading politician. I was shown the cunningly captured photograph of the shining couple and duly purchased a paper. In the blurb, it stated that part of the honeymoon would be spent in Scotland at the ancestral home. I hoped she would not know of this, but I was wrong.

It must have been a week later. I was struggling with the development of my piece, and I thought I'd step outside for some fresh air. The wind carried raised voices and an eerie sobbing that seemed to gather to a pitch of pain. When I stepped forward, I could see them. She was shouting and crying in a voice I had never heard before, twisting and curling her body around where he stood. He was shouting back. Suddenly, they launched themselves into an intense embrace then withdrew into the cottage. When they emerged, they seemed calm. She handed him a mug with one of her potions, I presumed, and they sat outside drinking in the late afternoon sun. I saw him leave, turn and wave as he lolloped over the headland.

I chose not to be alone that night. At the Fishers' Inn, the atmosphere seemed subdued. I asked if everything was all right.

"You've not heard the news then?" my barman asked.

"What news?"

"It was on the radio. The young laird is very ill not like to survive and him jist married. They said he had taken some dried mushroom stuff as a health drink and some of it must have been poison. You can never tell with that fungi," he said, his voice full of despising.

I walked with quick steps out of the village, stumbling over the stones of the path. The moon was already up casting its glow over the waves, which slid like liquid pitch beneath, slap, slapping on the shore. The wind had died to a quiet hiss and fall, hiss and fall. I was too late. I saw the gloomy pile of her discarded clothes on the sand, the dark head of her hair streaming free down her back. The paleness of her figure slipped into the waves, further and further into the black water of the sea until I could no longer distinguish the dot of her head rising on my horizon. I shouted, but my voice was lost on the wind. By daylight, before the tide could erase it, I found one word written on the beach.

'Sorry.'

Water Wings

The tinny speaker spun out the music of the latest popular song, Tulips from Amsterdam. The child placed the bag on the wooden slats of the bench in the changing room. She sorted out the contents in a row, first the red ribbed bathing suit, then the rolled-up towel, then the tight white rubber cap and last, the orange water wings. Ugh! They smelled hot and oily! She extracted her skinny toes from the solid leather sandals and gazed at them. She counted: This little piggy went to market, this little piggy stayed at home, this little piggy ate roast beef, this little piggy had none, and this little piggy ran wee, wee, wee, all the way home, twice, quite slowly. Now it was alright, she could get undressed.

What was it her mother had said? "Oh Elspeth, do go to the pool and amuse yourself. Try to improve your swimming. I don't want to see you for at least two hours." Her mother's voice was cross, but she couldn't understand her face. It was often like that. When she asked the lady in the kiosk at the pool, who was always crocheting a white garment, what she was making, the lady said, "Nane of your business, hen." and screwed up her face. Elspeth didn't know what she had done.

Mummy seemed cross a lot, especially when Elspeth needed to count or refused to go into her room until all her dolls were in their proper positions with Teddy in the middle. She heard Maggie, when she was washing the floor, tell Tilly the cook that Mrs Avery-Smith was in a delicate condition and would require more help than usual. But when she asked them what a delicate condition was, Maggie said, "Little pitchers have long ears and shouldn't listen at doors." This was unfair because she didn't know what that meant either.

She could have asked Daddy when seated on his knee rubbed up

9

against his tweed jacket smelling his cigarettes, but he was always away in Edinburgh or London at his big office. Perhaps they meant like the china teapot she had broken by accident. Did that mean Mummy would break? What would make Mummy break into lots of little jagged pieces? How would she make Mummy break? She didn't know how to stop breaking Mummy and Elspeth wanted to be a good girl. It was all very puzzling. She heard the echoing sound of the music in the stone passage, outside. Would that man be there? She shivered as she began to pull off her jersey.

It was cold on her feet as she padded along the corridor past the changing cubicles. She pretended she was a bear walking on the icy snow of the pole, her skin tingling, burning with the frost. 'One, two, three, four, see how I go!'

There was a dip in the stone to form a pool. She splashed through the water. It had a funny smell, like the caustic soda Maggie used to clean the sinks. It worried her nostrils like strong smoke. She thought it would be a horrid green colour like the mist in Peter Pan when she went to the theatre. Mummy said they had started adding a substance called chlorine because it killed germs and was important because everybody carried germs on their bodies. Elspeth looked at the boy and girl who had just passed her and imagined germs, big black bugs crawling all over them, washed off to make black soupy water at her feet. Ugh! She lifted her legs as high as she could. 'One step, Two steps, Three steps, Four!' She was safely through the archway and into the reassuring sunshine.

It was almost the end of the holidays but still quite warm. Mummy said children did not experience the cold in the same way as grownups and could play on the beach for hours. Elspeth didn't really know what Mummy meant. Elspeth did feel cold sometimes. For instance, she was supposed to go and stand under the metal posts by the side and turn the handle so that she had a shower before bathing. She knew she wasn't going to do that because the water from the shower was dark blue and like drops from an icicle.

Tum tee, Tum tee tum tee tum! The music had changed to a Scottish dance tune. She knew that one, so she would walk in a square, pas de bas, pas de bas, before going into the water. A couple of gulls were screaming witchlike howls from the roof of the building. Probably, they were fighting over a stolen piece of bread or a dropped ice cream cone. She looked round the tiered sides of the pool where the spectators sat, rings and rings of stone seats just like that picture in her book on the ancient Romans of an amphitheatre called the Colosseum where they watched lions and people being killed. She closed her eyes and pretended the noise the gulls were making was the same as the Romans would have heard. She shivered again. She could see a few people sitting there: a man with a red face and his head covered by a hankie; a couple who were holding hands and not looking at the swimmers; an old lady with silver hair who was grunting and had her eyes closed. Perhaps she was asleep.

When Daddy looked like that, sitting in his chair after dinner with his glass of port, Mummy said to her not to shake him or ask him anything. "Let sleeping dogs lie," she said, though they didn't have a dog or one that was sleeping or lying. Elspeth had been especially puzzled and had to do her rhyme and walking time twice till she felt better.

There was another lady who was knitting a big red piece of wool. Perhaps she was like Maggie and made squares for a blanket for the poor people in Africa. She had seen Africa on the map at Sunday school. She thought of it as a big curly horn full of all the black people being covered by an enormous woolly blanket of multicoloured squares. Yes, the man with the pulled down hat and the raincoat was there. He was always there, she thought, and he always looked at her when she came. Now he raised his hand and waved. She looked down at her own little brown hand with the white scar where she grazed it on her tricycle and raised it in reply.

'One, two, three, four, five six, pick up sticks' took her over to the steps at the shallow end. The water was blue with squiggles which she knew was because of painting on the bottom but it seemed to her that she was in the middle of an ice lollipop which smelled of seaweed. In the winter, the big waves sometimes splashed over the sides and left deposits. Tilly said there was a story that a seal was swept over one year and had to be taken to Edinburgh Zoo, but Mummy said it was not true. When Elspeth came out, she smelled her own skin all encrusted with salt. That must be how a seal smelled all the time. Yuck!

Carefully, she adjusted the water wings and 'one, two, three, four, five, I can't dive' took her into the water. She gasped as the cold arms of seawater wrapped round her body up to her chest. Then, with 'one, two, three, in the deep blue sea' she raised her legs and kicked and with 'one, two, one, two, this is what I do' she carved a v with her hands as she had been taught. She kept her head up like a startled bird because she didn't like the salty taste of the water and the sting in her eyes. She decided to swim across the pool. A boy ploughed beside her, drenching her with spray. She lost her balance for a moment and swallowed some nasty green. "Go away," she hissed but he did not hear her. She ignored the other children playing in the shallows and swam to the deep end where there were less people.

She really didn't need her water wings any more, but she did feel better if she kept close to the side where there was an indentation in the stone, so she could hold on if she needed. She felt the rubber of the floats gripping her arms and buoying her up. Tulips from Amsterdam was playing again, and she could almost swim to the rhythm of the music. The sun was melting the cap on her head and the water round her tummy was warmer now, almost like her bath at home.

Suddenly, a huge black shape came diving down on top of her and she was under the blue squiggles. They were pressing down on her and she was swallowing the heavy blueness until she couldn't breathe anymore and there was a great pain in her chest. And then she was on the surface, spitting and heaving, and she could see the light blue sky above with the cloud that was shaped like Africa. Immediately above her was a face and then strong arms were pulling her out onto the side.

"Are you alright, little girl? That chap had no business to dive at that moment, but I don't think he even saw you. Good thing, I was watching. I don't think anyone noticed."

She nodded. She thought she was like the kitten the gardener had tried to drown, all streaming fur and almost closed eyes. It was that man, only he didn't have on his raincoat and he must have left his hat on the seat. He had on grey flannel trousers and what Mummy would call a nice white shirt. She realised she was shivering and couldn't stop even if she tried to hold a breath and count. His big hands tight on her arms were pulling her towards the entrance to the changing rooms.

"Let's get you warm and dry and safe."

She was numb with shock and cold, her body like a frozen cadaver in a crevasse. He swept up her towel from the seat on the way and wrapped it round her shoulders and hurried her through the stone corridor to where the men's and women's changing rooms divided.

And that was where it happened. His wet tongue was fire. His hands hot under her tight wet bathing suit shoving and pushing. She had no voice to shout or scream and anyway, there was no one there to hear. The crocheting lady had gone for her tea break. But Elspeth was able to sink her teeth into his arm until the blood spurted warm and disgusting into her mouth, like salt tea. She wriggled her slippery thin body out of his grasp and ran quicksilver

13

away from him into the sunlight and the sounds of swimmers carving their passage through echoing splashes to the never-ending Amsterdam music.

No one observed the child counting her steps to the deep end, tearing the orange water wings from her arms and throwing herself into the wiggly worms of comforting blue.

The Oyster of Love

I touch the crenated cover of the creature.
My fingers move down the crenellations
Of your spine.
I like those crags.

 I hear the wind of waves, breathe the brine,
Lick the salt of our lovemaking.
Like the mollusc, you are bonded
With the sea.

 I cradle the crepuscular crustacean in my hand.
The storms have bruised its skin green-brown.
You rock me
From my despair.

 The encrusted casing is brittle but enduring.
Only grit has irritated the edges.
Can we withstand, together,
For as long as we can?

 With the sharpness of my knife,
I cut through the hardness,
And penetrate.
 The lips of opaline lie open.

The heart is pulsing.
 Clasping the shell to my mouth,
I drink the umbilical liquid.
I swallowed my pearl.

Auld Year's Nicht

Tap tap-tap, tap, tap tap-tap, tap! 'Should auld acquaintance be forgot,' he hummed to the rhythm under his breath.

"Will that be him, Mr McPhee, the last customer o' the year; the one you told me about?" She sniffed, loudly.

He looked at his assistant and sighed. Her eyes glistened under her permed hair. Little curls like tightly wound maggots, framed a wide and startled face. Her bosoms heaved under the constraints of her flowered apron, and her large elbows were planted on the counter, though he had specifically instructed her not to sully the polished surface. He had had doubts about engaging an assistant, but he knew the time had come when he could no longer manage on his own.

He looked round the shop, at the shelves crowded with glass jars of coloured sweeties in vivid colours: red love-hearts; green soor plooms; cinnamon; striped candy-balls; rows of tins balanced upon each other like gymnasts in a triangular tower; tins of spam, corned-beef, peas and beans. There were magazines stacked in picture piles; and leaning drunkenly against them the remaining Broons' annuals (The Broons, this year and Oor Wullie, next year). Neatly stacked boxes of cigarettes, Players, Marlborough, Gold Tipped, sat beside the occasional cigar, not that there was much call for them by his clientele, but the tobacco in the jars was popular and he had a good selection of polished wood pipes. His eyes travelled further, to the chocolate case with the bars of Fry's Cream, Five boys and Cadbury Dairy Milk and the tray of liquorice bootstraps which the bairns loved so much. Finally, there were the newspapers slotted into the new contraption he had recently purchased.

When his father died, it had never occurred to him to do anything different. He kept the business going: McPhee and Son, General Purveyors and Newsagents, By Appointment to His Majesty (well, they delivered to the Palace down the hill), Edinburgh, Athens of the North. It was a lucrative wee business in a prestigious position. Aye, well, the snell wind from Salisbury Crags had blawn them some good, right enough, but the question of his issue had troubled him before Mhairi passed away and afterwards he couldn't bear to think. Now it was the end of the year, time to reflect. There were the nephews, but they weren't interested, young scallywags. He sighed. He wasn't getting any younger.

Maggie sniffed again. She was a good enough soul, but he wished she didn't have that irritating habit, or that inquisitive nature, always wanting to know about the customers.

"Folk will tell you their business in their own good time if they want you to know it," he told her.

Tap, tap, tap - the sound of a stick on icy cobbles.

"Aye, Maggie, that will probably be him and I think he'll be the last one for tonight."

Why did he say that? He knew he would be the last. He always was. He went to the door and opened it in order to peer up the close, letting in a cold blast of sooty swirling air as he did this. He could smell the sour odour of fog and frost and see the thick particles hanging in a suspended cloud under the orange light of the streetlamp rimed by white. The snow had frozen into a ruff around the ironwork.

In the other direction, down the dark steps that descended to Waverley Station, he could make out a dim red glow beyond the curtain of black. 'Hellfire must look like this,' he thought, knowing well enough that the glow came from the burners that kept the points functioning.

A screech like a banshee was followed by a low, dull boom. He shivered. He remembered the way his heart used to jump in the War when he heard the sound. Here in Edinburgh they were lucky, not like the poor souls in Port Glasgow.

Screech, whistle!

That would be the last train of the year arriving at its destination. He could imagine the big black engine spitting steam like a dragon halted in its tracks, the train disgorging its passengers from the carriages, a dark sea of men in Homburg hats and Mackintoshes, and tweed-suited ladies, hats squashed on their hairdos, wrapping wool coat cocoons around themselves, scurrying into the night. Everyone would want to be home for Hogmanay. The station staff would be relieved. No trains, the morn. Tomorrow would be a day of rest, the Ne'erday holiday.

It was unlikely that any of these folk would come up this way and want to buy a paper or some tobacco.

Tap, tap, tap, tap. Looking to his right, he could faintly discern a figure at the head of the close. It was strange that all the other sounds seemed muffled by the fog, as though a blanket was holding them in a woolly grasp, yet the sound of the silver-handled cane on the setts of the Old Town was as clear as ice breaking from the gutter above. He closed the door and turned back to the interior of the shop with its unique smell of newsprint and candles mixed with the acrid scent of paraffin from the heater in the corner which did little to dispel the damp chill.

"Mr Auld, you called him, a wee man with a black hat and whiskers, not one of our real regulars but a regular nonetheless. And we must make sure he has a copy of the last edition of the year, for there is only one on Hogmanay. You said he's been coming to the shop for as long as you can remember and your faither told you about him because he came in his time. He must be a good age then, Mr

McPhee, begging your pardon? He has a big black coat and walks wi a stick and I should be awfy polite. Isn't that right, Mr McPhee? But whae is he? Does he bide near here?" Maggie's words rattled out like a catechism well-learned, but her nose was red and inquisitive.

Suddenly, he had had enough.

"Maggie, it's the last day of the year and it's fair late in the day. It is Ne'erday tomorrow and you must be needing to get home to your mother. I'll be shutting up in another ten minutes. You get away now and here's a wee something to add to your wages, just in recognition of the season. Happy New Year when it comes, Maggie, and I'll be seeing you after the holiday, the back of eight o'clock sharp, mind, Maggie."

He passed a buff envelope to her and extended his hand to Maggie who pumped it with her moist, pink fingers.

"That's awfy guid o'ye, Mr McPhee, and a Happy New Year to you when it comes."

She made the usual palaver of unwinding her overall and pulling on her boots, before donning her old warm coat and tying her headscarf. But despite her lingering desire to see the stranger, she was out the door and away down the steps before the tap, tapping stopped outside.

Then the shop door swung open with a twang of the bell. Mr McPhee waited alert behind the counter as the wee man in the long, old-fashioned coat approached him. The fog so pervaded the shop that the outlines of everything were fuzzy. The light was very dim. The light bulb seemed to be sputtering its last. He must remember to replace it.

He could scarcely make out the features in the wrinkled face, though the eyes were bright enough. The hand clothed in a black

19

leather glove was imperious as it pointed to the newspaper stand. Hurriedly, Mr McPhee selected the latest edition of "The News", the last of the old year, and thrust it at his customer who produced a shining sixpence from his pocket with the fine, delicate white fingers from which he had peeled the glove. Did he imagine the whispered and husky tone of "I thank you and goodnight."?

The wee man was out of the door before Mr McPhee had time to finish his "Thank you, Mr Auld, and Happy New Year to you, too."

It was odd, he thought, that he never had known for sure that this was the wee man's name. It was what his father had called him; Mr Auld, the man who aye came in for the last edition of "The News" on Hogmanay and whom they never seemed to see from one year's end to the next.

As a boy, it was a seasonal ritual to be told, "Mind and keep a paper back for Mister Auld. He'll be the last customer we'll see this side o' the year."

Nobody knew anything about him, which was strange in this part of the town where the tenements teemed with life and abody looked after abody's bairns. He couldn't be local then. A visitor for the New Year, perhaps? But that was queer in itself in the Auld Toon. Once, long ago, he had asked Mrs Laing, the auld biddie who had lived all her days in the Lawnmarket. "Would you know a Mister Auld? He aye comes here on Auld Year's Nicht. He keeps himself very close, a wee man with whiskers, a hat, a big black coat and a silver handled stick?"

"Noo ye're asking, Mr McPhee."

She sucked in her breath with a noise like the plunger coming out of the bath and wrinkled the deep furrows of experience on her face.

"Naw. I've kent them a', man and bairn as bides hereabouts, but nane like thon ye're talking aboot. D'ye ken if he bides south o'the Tron?"

And of course, he didn't, and was sorry he had asked.

He could not say what prompted his rush of curiosity. Did it spring from Maggie's questions; his own reflections; his morbidity at this particular time on this particular year? He could not say, but he had this unaccountable urge to find out more about the wee man as he heard the steady beat of the stick on the cobbles. He rushed to take off his cloth coat, replace the lid of the counter, douse the stove, rattle the shutters closed and don his tartan muffler, outdoor coat and cap.

He came out of the shop into the gloom just as the darker shadow of a figure seemed to reach the top of the close with a tap, tap, tap. He followed as quickly as he could, picking his way among the puddles of frozen snow greasing the paving. As he emerged into the wider street, he saw the wee man cross brusquely to the other side and slip between the well-lit portals of the World's End Pub, from where the sound of music and raucous laughter was an indication that a lively evening was already in progress.

Now Robert McPhee was not averse to the odd dram consumed in the comfort of his kitchen, or with an old crony, but he seldom entered a public house, and, in any event, he had been planning a nice wee evening by the fire at home with his slippers and a glass of malt. At midnight, after listening to the bells on the radio, he would take his coal and his whisky to his neighbours. Jean McDougall made a good black bun and shortbread, and Donald and he could have a good crack, then it would be back to bed with his hot water bottles and a long-lie in the morning with no papers to see to.

But he felt himself drawn to follow the wee man.

A fetid fug of cigarette smoke and the smell of human bodies met him. The place was heaving with customers, jostling, shouting and laughing. The light was poor, and the ceiling was festooned with paper chains and swinging bells, so he found it difficult to adjust his eyes. He pushed past a large man with a tiny tinsel crown on his bald head.

"Watch whaur ye'r gaun Jimmy!"

"I said, 'Excuse me', but you didn't hear," he muttered, but they were all three sheets to the wind.

He found himself at the circular bar with the fake Christmas tree with its red, blue and green fairy lights balanced on the counter. Just beyond, draped round their bar stools, a couple of sailors leaned over two young office girls, their breasts captured in their brassieres, pointed like little conical bings under tight blouses, lipstick slashed red on their mouths, skirts hitched to show off their nylon clad legs. One had heavy eyes and was swaying to the playing of the man with the squeeze-box in the corner. She looked as though she might fall off her stool. And the sailor laddie, he was peering down her cleavage as if to the ocean depths. And what was his other hand doing? Taking advantage, in a public place! Disgusting!

Then he saw the object of his quest, sitting in the corner by the accordion player, at a table all on his own. He too was watching the group. The wee man had a smile on his face – he was leering!

"What can I get you, sir?" He looked at the barman in some puzzlement and then collected himself.

"A dram of Whyte and Black, please and do you see thon wee man in black in the corner? Does he come here, often? D'you know him?"

"Mister, on the busiest nicht o'the year, I dinnae hae time to be fashed wi questions. That'll be five shillings." Then he relented a little, "Onyway, I dinnae ken who you're talking aboot."

Robert McPhee took a long sip of his drink. He could feel the cool liquid turn to fire in his throat and slide to his loins, the smoke of the barley at the back of his nose. He lifted his head from his glass and looked into the corner. Mr Auld was gone!

After another awkward struggle to the door, he reached it in time to hear the relentless tapping and to see the dark figure cross the street further down. 'He's bound for the Tolbooth Bar,' he thought, and he was right.

The Tolbooth Bar was quieter, probably because the landlord wouldn't allow the local populace any "tic". There was the usual crowd of cronies sitting and playing dominoes in front of the red coals of the fire, with the sparks glinting off the cast iron surround and brass fire irons. The Tolbooth was always dark and gloomy, though they had made an effort at seasonal cheer with the odd bit of holly over the pictures.

It wasn't until he had settled himself at a table under the window with another dram that he saw him in an alcove in the shadows, alone with a glass of something red. Robert started to rise with the vague intention of joining the wee man when he was stopped in his tracks by a cry from the group as a man staggered forward with blood coursing down his face, and lurched out onto the pavement. There was a stream of invective as another ran in pursuit, followed by the dull thud of bodies locked in an unnatural embrace. The place was all commotion as the other cronies raised their voices and the landlord tried to summon the local constable, but Robert saw his wee man grinning as he slipped out of the side door. Robert downed his glass.

Although he wanted to go home, to be away from this wildness, he felt compelled to follow as the wee man turned up the road and off into the Royal Ensign. No sooner had Robert enjoyed a few swallows of the fiery liquid at the Ensign, then another row broke out. This time it was a husband and wife, a drunken domestic altercation with her screaming, him pulling out great tufts of lank hair, and her gouging his face with her nails until it flowed burns of blood.

'Deil tak this place,' he thought. 'The public houses of the High Street were a veritable Hell on a holiday!'

He needed to head home but was feeling light-headed and knew that he should eat before walking to the tram, yet somehow, he found himself in the Burke and Hare, with a double he did not remember ordering. The barman was calling time. The crowd was very merry, talking about going out to wait at the Tron Kirk for the bells. Their voices jangled in his head like the bells themselves.

Then he saw the wee man at the back of the pub, where the dart-board hung with a piece of tinsel framing it. He was no longer making any attempt to conceal himself. Indeed, he was gyrating about, doing a wee Highland Fling. And then Robert saw the strangest thing; the shape of a body with a dart sticking out from the chest lay at the feet of the wee man.

He couldn't be sure it wasn't a dream, because there was a great crush of people wanting to leave the place and they were carrying him with them. Then he felt the crush in his chest. The bell was beating, tap, tap, tapping in his ribcage. He couldn't feel his arm any more. There was red behind his eyes, and then the pain was so great, everything seemed to be going black – yet the light outside was hard and white as if the frost and fog were illuminated from below. Perhaps the Council had rigged up extra lighting for the New Year?

A great crowd of people pressed around him. They were chanting a countdown. A piper was droning his bag in readiness as they watched the clock.

Robert saw the wee man was standing so close, he could have touched his coat, and the wee man turned and looked at him with a smile, putting his finger on the side of his nose. Did he imagine the whispered, "Happy New Year, Robert McPhee!?"

The figure melted into the dispersing crowd, but Robert saw the newspaper flutter to the ground and he retrieved it. It was folded at the announcements page. Under the lamp light, he could see one name had been surrounded by a black border. "Auld, Nicholas 31st December." But the remainder of the date was missing.

Hogmanay

The dying year cracks ice,
Brittle as a wishbone.
A flake of fear
Drifts in the cold air.
Pale corporal snow dissolves
With intentions.
The year folds in on itself;
A body doubled with doubt,
And desire
For a new beginning.

Dans l'herbe

She looked at her surroundings with a sense of satisfaction. The wallpaper with its trellis design of bright green foliage and tiny red insects emphasising the kind of exotic jungle one could find only in the rural gardens of southern France. It was just right, exactly as she had designed it. You could almost hear the hum of the insects munching. It provided a delicious haven for the customer entering from the cold winter streets of London. The slow strains of Debussy or Ravel seduced them as they settled in their seats at tables covered in verdant damask cloths nestling among potted palms.

She cast a careful eye over the settings and mentally shifted the faux Art Nouveau condiments a quarter of an inch from the perfect cones of garnet linen napkins. The twisted grasses in the long glass holders were not quite as she intended. Perhaps she would change her florist? However, the discreet murmurings of her French staff were entirely pleasing as they sashayed between the tables like gadflies in their green suits, attentive but not overpowering, lulling the customers into a dreamlike state where they would spend more and more and more!

Dans l'herbe was her first baby, her flagship restaurant. Yes, she had made the right decision to bring him here. It was time to tell him in her perfect setting.

"Madame Mantissa, everything is to your satisfaction, I hope?"

Pierre, her restaurant manager, looked at her expectantly. He paused briefly to allow her to incline her head slightly in affirmation before he continued, dropping his voice to a mere whisper.

"We are prepared for your guest, Madame. Monsieur Davide has

27

been very busy in the kitchen and all is as you ordered down to the finest detail, I can assure you. It is always a pleasure to serve you, Madame."

"Thank you, Pierre. Perhaps you can bring the aperitifs in anticipation?" Her voice was sweet but crisp with a faint hint of green apple acidity.

"Very well, Madame."

She smiled as she watched his gangly body glide away like a lizard along a stalk.

For a minute, she caught sight of her reflection in the mirrors on the wall, behind the spouting faun fountain to her left. She smiled again. Perfect! She had chosen her dress to be understated yet to make a statement, a simple figure moulding shift of fine wool in raspberry red with green piping. Her hair, which was coloured a similar shade, was cut short and at angles to expose her high cheekbones. What a fuss her hairdresser, Kevin, had made! "Ooh, Melissa, you simply cannot be serious!" But she paid the piper to play her tune and she knew it was absolutely right. She stretched out her legs and regarded her Louis Vuitton shoes, an impulse buy. She deplored giving way to sudden desires but with these shoes she had no regrets. They were soft crocodile leather, green, simple with just one detail, the raspberry-red killer heels. She placed her hands on the table in her habitual mode, raised together, red nails touching, emerald and ruby rings glinting, a praying position which was not humble.

"Madame?"

Pierre slid the glasses expertly from his silver tray onto the tablecloth, one red one green in their frosted flutes.

"That is correct, Pierre, the Campari is for Monsieur (always so pedestrian, she could have added) and the Crème de Menthe is for me."

She nibbled an almond which had just the right amount of bitterness. It was just as well, she thought, that she was not allergic to nuts like some people!

He was late. How typical! Really his behaviour was intolerable! Well, this would be the last time. Her mind wandered. Always she created a new signature dish afterwards. It must include elements of green and elements of red. No spice, chilli or paprika in this case. They were not appropriate. Something with water, a soft glutinous texture, perhaps a watercress coulis dribbled around a stuffed red fruit of some description. What was the name of that vivid Brazilian fruit with the snake-like skin? The stuffing could be minced sweetbreads bound together with hazel nuts, heather honey and oil, flavoured with Campari, to add a touch of bitterness and set off the almost cloying sweetness of the rest. Of course, it would be decorated with French parsley in the vivid green she loved.

"Melissa Mantissa, darling, you look wonderful! Why didn't they tell me when I booked?"

She was confronted by a broad-boned ageing man, immaculately dressed in a camel coloured cashmere suit, a deep pink tailored shirt with a silk coffee coloured cravat at the neck and a pink handkerchief in his top pocket. His jowls were still heavy, but his clothes seemed to hang on his bones as though the flesh beneath had shrunk. She immediately recognised the ghastly guru of gourmet restaurants, the well-known writer and cynic, charming at the table but vitriolic in print. She remembered he had been very seriously ill but had made a remarkable recovery. Some sort of seafood allergy, she recalled.

She smiled a tight little smile of welcome, rose and allowed herself to be kissed on both cheeks, "Richard, how lovely to see you. I hope you are well?"

"My dear, I couldn't be better after the ministrations of my darling fiancé. He booked your delightful restaurant as a teeny surprise and of course some very special friends will be joining us. I hope that you will join our little party."

"Forgive me, Richard, I am meeting someone. I have a business meeting, a final contract which I must conduct in private."

"Of course, my dear, you are the perfect businesswoman. Oh, there's Michael, I must welcome him." And he was off across the room, throwing his arms out in embrace.

She had just resumed her seat when her special guest arrived. She felt the warmth of his fingers on her shoulders as he bent to kiss her neck whispering,

"Darling Melissa." For a brief moment she felt her own flesh respond, but not for long. "I am ravenous. I am dying to know what you have planned for me, my darling."

He folded his long limbs into the seat opposite. He had dressed with care to match his surroundings, casual in green designer jeans and shirt with a blood coloured pullover. She liked him for that, but then she did pay him well.

"I've ordered a very special menu. You are late, very late."

"Sorry Melissa, I've been in meetings all morning, doing business for you, by the way. You know how it is and I know how you abhor mobiles in the restaurant so there no point in texting. Forgive?"

She knew he was lying. She had checked of course. His hair flopped forward on his handsome face and hid his green eyes with their alluring gaze. He knew this was an endearing pose, that of the

30

naughty student.

"Melissa, you look fantastic, by the way."

She nodded and waved to the waiter.

The amuse bouche arrived with the bottle of Dom Perrier: little glass boats in which lay a green mollusc on a tiny toast; a petit tart of caviar covered in a green cream; a little round deep pink ball of fried prawn and a tiny potato cake with red pomegranate seeds.

He addressed the glistening mollusc offering with relish. "Do you have these flown in from New Zealand specially, Melissa?"

"Be careful. Savour the moment," she said. Some silvery green flecks stuck to his teeth as he talked. Repulsive, really. She had made the right decision. They talked of personalities in the business in vague terms as they consumed the green pea and Chablis soup with the bright pink lobster dumplings.

It was not until the main course, a symphony of seafood on a plate which was itself worthy of a gallery exhibition, that she told him that his services would no longer be required. He did not appear to hear her. Instead, he reached for the pearl oyster covered in a green mayonnaise and poised in its shell as part of the picture on a plate.

"One must always swallow in a oner," he said as he tipped it down his throat.

She heard the little gasps which rippled through his chest and then mounted to a crescendo of escaping air before he slumped upon the table. His greenish pallor changed to bright red and back as she watched. It was all over in a moment. As the waiters rushed to the table, she observed in clear tones,

"Oh dear it does sometimes happen that people do develop a sudden allergy to oysters in Dans L'herbe and I'm afraid there is nothing to be done!"

Bad Hair Day

The man shuffles past the notices of perms.
His hair hangs tangled, matted, dirty black.
My brush pushes the discarded curls back.
Dead hair like cat's fur gathers germs.

I smell the warm, dry chemicals of my trade.
Smoke now fills my nostrils with intensity.
In my head explodes a bonfire of vanity,
Like those piles of burnt leaves I made.

I crash out of the door; gulp a great gasp,
Fall over the dreadlocked tramp in a mound.
My mind is muddled with a siren's sound.
"Can I give you a haircut, now?" I rasp.

"Wot you want then, lady?" His eyes are mean.
I open my mouth and scream and scream!

Muchas Gracias

"Thaat's right. C'mon! C'mon! Gie it a wee bit mair lalldy!" His voice was loud and coarse.

She winced and could feel the skin around her eyes and nose tighten despite the generous layer of suncream which she had spread on her skin, like fertiliser on a field, that morning. Well, with the dangers of skin cancer one couldn't be too careful, though she suspected she had some Norwegian heritage as her skin was a golden apple colour rather than prurient pink. In fact, she thought she benefited from some exposure to sun as she looked at her lean arms stretched along the lounger. The skin beneath her bathing suit straps was scarcely wrinkled and there were no liver spots, just a satisfactory bronzing.

"Go! Go! C'mon hen! This is no Ayr races but ye could gie it a better shot!"

Her body tensed. What on earth was that ridiculous boy doing now? He made her wince. Wince, now that was an interesting word, so appropriate for that sense of compression and disgust that affected one's whole being. She must look up the source in the dictionary. Was it Anglo Saxon? No probably French. Wince like pince. Pince-nez, that was certainly French.

Really, she should know but it was hot and a delicious feeling of lethargy was creeping over her. If she closed her eyes, she would hear the humming of the insects in the bougainvillea which tumbled magenta pink, lilac and vibrant orange over the railings; the constant call of the birds in the orchard terraces below; the trilling of the canary in its cage on the balcony above which had upset her at first. Why must the Spaniards confine these poor little bundles of fluff? Now it seemed part of the atmosphere, along with the gentle lap of the pool by her side. No one was swimming yet. Too soon after breakfast she supposed. And that noisy family with the children must have departed or gone to the beach.

"Well Rhona, I just think Linda had a lucky escape. He was a monster incarnate, was he not? But tell her that!"

The words brushed space like a crude daub of paint on a canvas, hanging seconds before dripping in little rivulets of revulsion.

"But Marie, they had even signed a pre-marriage contract and, of course, the second time around!"

She could hear them and smell their expensive perfume here, downwind. Two carefully coiffured ladies, from Westend or Southside Glasgow. One in a tiger skin bathing suit, the other in a black bikini with silver spangles. Both savouring the carcass of a marriage, or near-marriage, like jackals worrying at a piece of meat.

Oh dear! She knew a package had its dangers, but she had needed this holiday so much at the end of term. It had presented itself in the newspaper, a late deal with an exclusive company to a quiet resort and so convenient, flying from Glasgow. It was still quite expensive but not as dear as those retirement trips her friend, Shona, had suggested. At least at that dreadful final coffee morning, with a tight little smile, she had been able to say to staff that she would be moving on to exotic parts before settling down to a different routine. She could not tell them that she would need to invest every penny of her lump sum to provide enough income to maintain herself and the house and that life stretched as an empty void before her without work. Of course, she might pick up some day or evening classes but then, there would be so many others like her pushed out early by cuts at the Colleges who would be seeking similar employment. Of course, she should sell the house, a great sandstone edifice with too many rooms, but she just couldn't face it. Besides, the market was so low just now, who would want it?

34

Pity mother's money had all been swallowed up by private nursing care. No, she would stay put, and try to keep going. Perhaps she could rent out a room to a University student but then there would be their friends making a commotion, creating a mess and causing disruption. No, she could not tolerate that. She pushed these disagreeable thoughts away.

"I warned her, you know. He's just taking you for a ride. He's all side and no real depth. No class. You know what I mean? Well with his history...?"

On and on and on! Black bikini was clearly enjoying herself. Did the glitter on her costume match the malicious sparkle in her eyes, she wondered?

Had she herself been warned? Mother had asked, "Do you know what you want, darling?" And of course, she had thought it was what she desired. She conjured a picture of Henry in her head: the blue jeans, well cut; the pale blue shirt; the way his brown hair ruffled off his forehead; his slightly bemused smile; the way her flesh felt when he touched her. He was really a nice man and he had thought he loved her, but it wasn't enough. Oh, it was all such a disappointment. He was just so weak. She came to despise him.

And his mother was a monster. She remembered his gentle pleading. "We'll just stay a few months after the wedding until she feels a bit better." Well a few months was all she could take. She was still young enough. She thought it was the thing to do, and she thought she might still have a child. Maybe she also wanted to get away from home. Daddy was still alive, and Mummy didn't need her. Perhaps she was just Henry's little rebellion. They didn't really want or need each other. Life was better afterwards. The warmth of the sun on her skin reminded her of the sex. Yes, she had missed that at first but then it was never earth-shattering with Henry, and he was always so afraid Mother would hear their groans. Oh well, it was all so long ago. Not too many chances now?

"Yah wee beaut!"

She allowed herself a glare in the direction of the rude young man, though of course the effect would be lost because of her large sunglasses. She was rather proud of these glasses which were modish, unlike her previous pair, a late purchase at the airport. He really was impossible, with his loud language. A typical keelie type, ignoring everyone's privacy. He'd be swearing next. Well she had heard enough f...s from the students to last a lifetime and she wasn't about to put up with this on her holiday. She abandoned her book and looked directly at him.

Whatever was he doing? She observed that on the other side of the pool, he had set up an obstacle course of twigs, fallen hibiscus blossoms, a tube of sun-cream, a book. She squinted at its title. To her surprise, it was not a blockbuster but a classic, Rider Haggard. Over and around these things he was ushering a very large black beetle – a kind of Christopher Robin beetle, she thought – in what appeared to be some private race. She stared in some fascination as he finally scooped up the beetle to whom he had obviously ascribed female status and, with care, deposited her in the grass where she plodded off towards the jacaranda trees.

"It's like the hare an' the tortoise is it no? Slae bit sure."

She realised he had seen her watching and was now addressing her. The other two women were still deeply absorbed in their conversation. She nodded curtly and tried to convey that she was concentrating on looking at the view, which was indeed magnificent. Far below, over the red pan tiled roofs and curved Moorish chimneys of the resort, the narrow white streets of the old town clustered round the church on a promontory. She heard the slow dong of the bell call the seemingly timeless hours. Beyond were indigo smudges of sea which merged into an arc of never ending hyacinth blue sky.

"D'yu no fancy a wee dip? No need for a chittery bite here, eh? It's no like thae Sunday Skule outings tae Troon beach."

She inclined her head to acknowledge the communication but arranged her features in what she hoped was an aloof fashion in order to discourage future exchanges. Perhaps it had been effective since he lifted his towel from his chair, slung it around his shoulders in nonchalant fashion and headed for the shower by the steps to the pool.

How dare he make assumptions, talking about Sunday School as if she was of a certain age and experience! Yet despite herself she was intrigued. Hmm. He was really rather attractive looking. Not her type of course but his body was fair and freckled, well-toned without the beer belly she would have expected. Perhaps he did athletics or something. He was older than she had surmised at first, early forties perhaps, with quite a craggy face, high cheekbones, slightly hooked nose. His reddish-brown hair was just beginning to recede and thin on top though it was thick and crinkly elsewhere.

Splash! He had executed a neat dive at the deep end and emerged a sleek seal to carve a perfect curve with his crawl stroke to the other end. He swam a lazy series of effortless lengths then rested, brown torso balanced on the ceramic rim of tiles. She could feel his eyes directed at her with their blatant stare. Bother him! She took up her book, for once a rather trashy romance which Shona had passed to her as suitable holiday reading and pretended to be absorbed.

What did he see with that direct gaze? A woman in her prime or a woman past her prime, she corrected herself. While her figure was far from voluptuous, it was curvaceous. She knew those lewd boys in her class sometimes lusted after her. Once, she had found a not unflattering if exaggerated cartoon drawn in the margin of a test paper. The wee skellum! She had tried not to let it influence her marking. Trim, that's what Shona had said.

"You have a trim figure, Margaret, you shouldn't hide it away so much."

It was Shona who had persuaded her to buy the red wired bathing suit and the sarong decorated with red poppies.

She adjusted her sunhat and lowered her book. Sammy Seal was now performing handstands and somersault dives which produced glistening trails of bubbles on the surface. Really, he did seem able to hold his breath for a phenomenally long time under water, then surface, squeezing his eyes, water running in rivulets down his face, like the statue of some water god in the museum. Attention-seeking, that was his behaviour. Irritated but faintly flattered, she feigned total disinterest.

He was a conundrum. What on earth was this uneducated man doing on a holiday like this? At his age he should have a wife, a girlfriend like a bracelet dangling from his arm and a necklace of bawling children. Where did he get the money? Perhaps he was part of the Glasgow mafia. Everyone had read about the Ice Cream Wars and then of course there was the drug scene. She was only too aware of that with the students.

She gave a little snort as she thought about her disgust at those exploitative drug barons. Perhaps he was just out of jail. There was the merest frisson of excitement, and intrigue at the thought. Perhaps he was newly divorced and on the pull. Perhaps he was gay? No, he definitely wasn't. No. He didn't have the tight hips, or the walk, and he was interested in women. Well, in her.

Splash! First a hand thrust above the water a few feet from her – she could see a snake tattoo writhing around the wrist – waving at her and then a head shaken like a hound, a face with a cheeky grin and eyes. His eyes were quite arresting, she thought, dark with depths, astute but not unkind. Don't be stupid, Margaret. You see what you want to see.

"Well, missus al alain, are yu no comin in? The water's jist great, warm as onything. I bet yu were ane o thae weans that screamed like a banshee at yer christening. Noo's yer chance to prove somethin different. Hoo's aboot a wee paddle wi the waater King?" He gave a whoop and patted his not unhairy chest, then began to sing in a rather mellow baritone, 'I am sailing, I am sailing' imitating a Rod Stewart sway.

Out of the side of her eye she could see the Glasgow gossips had stopped talking and were watching. She wanted to smile at his antics, but he had gone too far. He was intrusive and presumptive, and she was not interested. Anyway, why did he keep referring to church. Oh Lord, perhaps he was some sort of happy clappy religious freak. No now was the moment for a put down.

She took her glasses off, gazed at him and speaking slowly as if she was instructing a recalcitrant and rather dim child, she enunciated,

"If you are addressing me, I have no intention of swimming in this pool until later, should I wish to do so. I will therefore not be joining Poseidon whom you so wish to emulate though I do not suppose you know who he is. I would also thank you not to interrupt my reading and disturb the peace of this place."

She felt the end was rather lame, so she jammed on her glasses firmly and seized up her book. There was the merest whisper of a giggle from the West-end group, but she was determined not to look in any direction,

He was discomfited and offended. She could tell by the roughness in his voice.

"Well hen if yu want to be Miss Uppity an miss oot on the

opportunity to be my Galatea, that's yoor loss. An by the way, a didnae come up the Clyde on a banana boat. Y'r no the only wan wi a classical education so put that in yr hoighty toighty pipe and smoke it!"

He was mixing his metaphors because he was angry, she thought. There was much noisy splashing as presumably he was cutting cross lines through the water, then silence. When she allowed herself to peer over her book, he was donning a rather elegant towelling robe and, without a glance in her direction, he marched off into the hotel lobby.

Oh dear, perhaps she had made an error of judgement – the old prejudices rising up like tongues of fire in her throat. But perhaps she had been right. Better to keep oneself to oneself. Anyway, that's what she wanted from this holiday: peace; time to restore her nerves torn and jagged on all those rocks of teaching; and to do precisely nothing; think of no one but herself. The lady tellers of misfortune had gone inside. She was utterly alone. Now was the perfect time for a dip and, then, perhaps another little sunbathe and relax. Relax.

"Signora, you want something?"

It was the waiter at her elbow. She must have drifted into a doze.

"Un cafè con leche, por favor." and she hesitated then added, "And a brandy." What the hell, she was on vacation!

"Si, Signora." He smiled almost conspiratorially. He was rather nice, this waiter she reflected, not obsequious but respectful. He had a friendly open face. He understood how to treat a lady on her own.

When he returned with her coffee and brandy, he presented her with the usual slip to be signed but she noticed another piece of hotel paper which she tried to give back to him as well. He refused to take it.

"No, no, Signora for you only" and smiling, he departed, humming and drumming a little rhythm on his silver tray. Flamenco.

Perhaps this was one of those invitations to a local show? She opened the paper and read.

"Dear beautiful Nymph, Galatea,

        Would you care to join me for a dander to the town, this evening? There is a rather good museum of archaeology and, nearby, an atmospheric but quiet bar which serves excellent tapas. Rendezvous at 5.30 in the lobby. Do please come.

All good waves,

Poseidon"

A little smile played on her lips. Well, well ... she just might.

To the waiter's retreating back, she called, "Muchas gracias!"

In the Pink

The insistent 'brrk brrk' of a grouse rattled through the October afternoon as he pressed himself against the heather and the damp peat, smelling the fungal warm scent of autumn that he loved so much. He lay prone as the sun stroked his back, his eyes scouring the moor for birds. Twenty years on the estate and he never tired of the job.

In front of him, a cool breath of wind parted the rustling fronds of brown bracken like a woman's skirt. A hot flush of emotion suffused his body from his boots to his ruddy face which glowed pink and perspiring under his deerstalker. The fibres of his tweed jacket burned into his back. He could feel his inner thighs, warm and wet. A terrible longing consumed him and would not let him go. He groaned from his troubled soul until his dog came to lick his black stained, salty fingers.

He had wanted them; desired them; craved them with a drug-user's desperation since he had first seen them, nestling in their tissue papered box; Mhairi's new shoes for the cousin's wedding in Campbeltown. Brilliant, sparkle-threaded, magenta pink with razor sharp pointed toes and rapier heels; they were his shoes!

"I think they'll look right fine, don't you?" she said as she twirled in her pink suit in front of the mirror. At that moment, he had hated his wife for being what he could never be. Then, his guilt gripped him, winding tendrils of ice around his tongue.

"Aye, jist fine," he had said, fixing his mouth into a grim smile.

They had married as teenagers not long after he found his first job as assistant gamekeeper. They had grown up, 'thegither' you might say, in this small island community. He loved her but not in the way she wanted. She had become used to the pattern of their lives.

He knew he was the centre of her wee world – they were a settled couple – well respected, normal. How could he break the brittle prism of their lives by telling her this thing?

The old stone croft was grey and silent as he returned in the lengthening shadows. He pulled off his boots in the porch and slung his pouch in a corner. The fire in the Aga was only a dark red ashy glow, and the kitchen was cool and empty. He found a note on the table. 'Gone to Oban with Jeannie McPhee. Back on the last ferry. You'll find your own tea.'

Heart pumping in his ears, he took the stairs in great leaps so that the old wooden bannister shook under the pressure of his grip. A stride took him into their salmon-pink painted bedroom. Pink was Mhairi's favourite colour. He stopped and paused in front of the battered mirror-fronted walnut wardrobe. Almost tentatively, he reached out, grasped and turned the brass handle and, mesmerised, watched the doors swing open to reveal the shelves below his shirts, neatly stacked with his wife's balled tights, bras and nylon underwear. Beneath the hanging dresses, at the foot of the wardrobe, he could see the new shoebox. A satisfied, happy sigh flooded his body as his fingers crept around the lid.

Sometime later, he sat precariously perched on the edge of the double bed, a stocky, heavy man with surprisingly elegant curvaceous calves and ankles. Slowly and delicately, he rolled the smooth black tights up his stubbly, inexpertly-shaved legs. He stood up. Twitching his Inverness charity shop skirt to remove a crease, he regarded his reflection. He had made up carefully. The long diamanté clip ear-rings shook and shimmered in the light of the bedside lamp. At last, the time was now! Trembling with little shivers of excitement, he sat on the bed and his head a ceilidh of delight, he fitted first one then the other magenta pink slipper. Gradually and deliberately, he rose to take a few tottering steps.

43

Then, balancing with care, he began to waltz gently in front of the dimly lit mirror.

Vaguely, he heard the dog bark. 'Perhaps a fox,' he thought. A discreet bang. Quick, soft footsteps on the stairs, and his wife stood silent in the door space.

He confronted her anguished face in the mirror.

There was an awkward moment, life suspended; neither could speak. Then Mhairi stepped into the room, stiff-legged as if on stilts, rocking from side to side to see the full state of her husband. Shock gave way to disbelief and in turn to laughter.

"Ye big fool! Whit the hell de ye think ye look like? If ye'd fancied goin' tae the weddin' as a wifie I'd let ye! Ye'd only tae ask. Those shoes must be killin' ye. They're a bit neat on me."

He remained speechless. She turned to go downstairs.

"I'll put the kettle on. Eh ... ye daft bugger."

He finally found his voice. "Aye, tea'll be good, Mhairi."

War with Weeds

It was a warm day in late spring and all the birds were singing, "Cheep, cheep, cheep!" and "Chi, Chi, Chi!" they trilled from the trees and bushes. There was the occasional, "Croak!" from a frog in the pond and the bumble bees were busy in the blossoms. The garden seemed very peaceful and pretty with its fresh green leaves and bright flowers. But if you listened very, very carefully, you could hear another noise so faint that it was scarcely discernible to the human ear. A kind of twittering, a thin, reedy, squeaking sound. A rustling, purring, panting, playing that sometimes seemed to increase in volume like a cloud of insects buzzing in the air around you, and then became soft like a faint breath of wind. It was the sound of the plants complaining.

"I am so scared," wailed the grey Lavender bush which grew beside the grass. "I can see Dandy Lion marching across the lawn and he's going to bring his friends to sit and make a carpet around me and that will look horrible."

Dandelion smirked, adjusting his yellow crown. "Nothing to fear, Lavender my dear! I'm a beautiful colour of acid yellow. I'm your bedfellow. I'll just sink a tap root and jump tootie, toot, toot and Lavender, there you are!"

"Oh go away and find somewhere else to play!" sighed the Lavender.

Meanwhile the Clovers were making advances to the Tulip bed. "Yo ho ho, here we go! Nice fresh earth, just right for us. Hear our mirth! Ha, ha, ha! We'll tangle and mangle and strangle. We're on the run. Oh what fun!"

The Tulips moaned and tried to shuffle their bulb roots closer together to make a blockade against the advancing green tangle.

45

"Please, please don't tease," they begged. "We're not common three-leaved scallywags like you. We are special and come from abroad and we don't know what to do." It was all in vain!

"I'm little and sweet and I've tiny feet. There's plenty of Thyme so the next move is mine," said the plant called Shepherd's Purse as she shook her white flower heads and jumped all over the Thyme.

The Thyme grumbled, "I've wandered and wandered all over the place on wall and path, but it seems that nowhere is safe."

"I know what you mean. I'll never be seen," said the Wallflower as he tried to push his scented head through a wall of Nettles, "Oh dear and there's a thing. These Nettles can sting!"

"Oh no, you cannot flee! Perhaps you know we make herbal tea? We're strong and useful, you see," sniggered the Nettles as they pushed down their roots and grew taller and taller.

"This is dreadful," sobbed Rose as she tried to push away the attentions of Sticky Willie who was cuddling up and attaching himself round her stems. "No matter how I prickle, you continue to tickle. Please go, oh do! I don't want to know you!" But Sticky Willie ignored her pleas.

At the same time, Bindweed had decided to choke Honeysuckle, reaching his long arms around her and twisting them higher and higher. "Oh fie, fie, fie! If you don't stop, I'm sure I'll die," screamed the poor plant.

A battle was continuing in the blue corner between the Pansies and the Buttercups.

"You belong in the field on the farm where you can't do any harm," shouted the Pansies, "Not in our nice bed!"

The buttercups, who were winning, laughed, "Get real, this is a steal! Now we're here we intend to stay for ever and a day!"

The Ground Elder was busy surrounding the Hawthorn tree who was looking decidedly unwell.

"Oh, never fear, we love it here," he crowed. "I've invited all my relatives as well, as you can tell."

Hawthorn, who should have been feeling his best as he came into blossom, wailed, "You're causing me so much pain; I'll never be the same again."

As they feared dying, the plants of the garden fell to weeping and sighing, until the wise herb, Sage, spoke up, "What we need is an action plan. And though I've never been a fan of other garden species, we must unite and fight!"

Cherry rustled her white blossoms causing them to fall like snow, "But what can we do? I belong to another party and have little in common with you." Many of the other plants nodded at this. Sage whispered to Rosemary, "She thinks she is a superior tree but she must see that now is the time for the garden plants to agree." He addressed The Garden, "We have much in common, even Grass Lawn and we have the same foe. The weeds must go!" There were shouts of agreement.

Honesty shouted out bravely from her dark corner, "Perhaps a solution is a coalition-that means different parts of the garden, despite their differences, working together for the good of all. We need to do something before we see more plants fall by the wall."

And so, it was agreed that all the plants should work together under a small group led by Sage to try to rid themselves of the nasty weeds. Fortunately, the weeds were so busy having a lovely time growing and increasing that they did not hear the garden plants communicating. But what should they do? How were they to oust the weeds?

Sage said, "We need aid when the weeds invade. This situation is dangerous, who can help us?"

It was Honesty who had the idea. From her quiet little corner, she called, "Ask the gardeners to come and take the weeds out, every one. If we call and call, they must hear us all."

And so it happened. Perhaps the gardeners could not hear but they knew it was time to help the plants, so they went into the garden with their trowels and spades and forks and removed the weeds even though they could not hear the garden plants talk.

The Weeping Tree

Once upon a time, there lived in the forest a beautiful tree. He knew he was very lovely. As he stretched his arms and branches to the sky, he tried to touch the blue of the heavens – though, of course, he couldn't hope to do this because, though he was very strong and tall, the sky was far, far away. He was proud and rather vain.

"Oh, I am such a magnificent tree, everyone must admire me," he shouted to the wind.

The Spirit of the Wood gave a little sigh of laughter as he tossed the branches of the tree.

"Pride comes before a fall! Oh tree, you need to think of someone other than yourself in this wood."

In the spring, his twigs bore little fluffy balls like rabbit tails which were soft and furry and were a kind of flower containing pollen. Later in the summer, the branches were covered in lush green leaves which were thin and pointed and very numerous. The tree waved his branches to the sky like banners in a breeze.

"Oh, look at me, I must be the finest tree in this wood," he boasted.

"Well, we'll see," whispered the Spirit.

The badgers played in the roots of the tree and sometimes an owl flew past his trunk in the night, screeching to the world as it went hunting. But no one bothered the tree and he cared for no one other than himself.

In the autumn, when his leaves turned first yellow and then brown, and the fierce gales shook them to the ground to lie in great heaps at the foot of his trunk, the tree was rather sad, but he knew that the cold winter would follow and he would have a nice long rest.

"Mmm, time for a good sleep to conserve my strength. I am really such an exceptional tree; I can have lovely dreams."

He stuck his bare black arms into the sky where the snowflakes drifted and settled on the twigs to the sound of his snoring, that was so quiet that only the Spirit of the Wood could hear it.

When the tree began to stir again, he could hear the birds begin to sing their spring tunes in his branches. Now, the tree liked a good melody, and he tried to push out his fluffy flowers in time to the music of their song. He particularly liked this time of year when he could feel the first warm rays of the sun. However, there was something different, something even more beautiful this year.

He listened to a trill of notes cascading from above in an exquisite cadenza and thought, 'This song must come from heaven, itself.' But then he saw it; a little black bird was perched on one of his branches singing its heart out, its chest pumping up and down with the effort. The tree thought the music was so beautiful he wanted to hear it again and again, and mostly the little black bird obliged, except at night when he had to rest.

"Please, please, little bird, come and live among my leaves which will soon grow, and you can stay with me forever. My long arms can give you protection. I need to hear your song which makes me so happy," said the tree, and the little bird cocked his head on one side and gazed at the tree with his bright eyes, and nodded. All through the summer they lived together in harmony, and the tree fell in love not only with the song of the little black bird, but with the black bird itself!

"Ah ha!" said the Spirit of the Wood.

The first frosts of autumn were just beginning to drain the colour from the leaves when a terrible thing happened. The tree was listening to the pure notes of his friend's song, when he heard the

50

whir of huge wings and a heavy weight fell through his branches, and the song stopped mid-phrase.

"What has happened? Where are you, little friend? Why don't you sing to me?" the tree asked. Then he bowed his head and looked down to the ground at his feet where, with a whoosh, a hawk took flight, leaving behind a little pile of bones and black feathers.

"It's only Nature's way," said the Spirit of the Wood. But the tree could not be consoled. He wept, and he wept for the loss of his friend.

In his sorrow everything about the tree drooped. He no longer reached into the sky. His arms flopped down until his twigs brushed the ground. His tears rolled down his trunk wetting the ground below and soon they formed a pool and the branches swirled patterns in the water.

"Oh where, where has my little black bird gone? I miss him and his song so much. I failed to protect him as I promised," he sobbed. "I was wrong to think it was important to be the best tree in the wood. I couldn't even help my friend."

"Never mind," said the Spirit of the Wood, "now he will be remembered always by the weeping tree you have become, and if you listen very carefully to the sound the sighing wind makes in your branches, only you will hear his notes. He will live with you forever, just as you asked."

And the tree listened. And his heart was lighter because he could hear his friend singing and could remember him.

The Crimblecrump Granthag Ball

'T'were twarig and spalid in the grantly granthag
Around the lodd, brathy fay the mantly massag
Clatch, platch, the crogs a crimble cargle guggle glog
Slithously, the Sarpagost snithelled a sniddle spog.

The pagruths pintled a puggy, gurdy, bughry bant
Minsly, mowsly, magansly, the moreths, intly mant
The flobberglobb finefft a foon samsy snin,
All fuddly sniddled gunts erbly-onkly in.

A Printhintcrick joomped and findled
Zingglezats zimped, zeeved and zindled
The Trinthums tinsed a prantig sig
While Finty Finglefals fleeped and flig.

The Snodel sindled silpy up
The Brodel brindled a bist bup
Cragricks trixillate a glant prum
Tonticks tronned a finty trum.

They twirgled and twargled, spingled and spargled
They frant and sast 'til all were obrously spaggled
Granthagers ristled and rivelled until mintel
When all fransig fativities fatig fintel.

Black Leaves

"Whoosh! Whoosh! Look what I can do to this bush," shouted the Autumn Wind as he scattered the dry brown leaves which had fallen from the branches of the Hawthorn hedge.

"It'll be winter soon and I'll have to change my tune," trilled the Blackbird in the apple tree.

"There are still nice berries for us to munch and crunch and I am having a particularly tasty lunch," sang the Thrush pushing out his speckled chest and selecting a red berry from a juicy bunch on the rowan twigs. "But winter is coming, beware. I feel it in my bones and we don't know how we'll fare."

The old Yew shook his mighty branches so that they shivered as the Wind passed over them. The Robin hopped onto one of the Yew's green arms and tried to console him.

"You have lived for years and years in the garden here and I'm sure you can have nothing to fear. We all realise that you are very old and very wise. As for me, I'll keep on my feet and eat and eat to survive and I know I can keep alive." And he flew down to the ground as he espied a delicious worm.

"Oh Yew, don't worry so and become too low. We Roses can take a lovely long nap and withdraw our sap very soon. When the cold snap comes, we lose every last bloom. My leaves are curling and dropping more every day but that is just Nature's way," said the Rose, Zephrine Droughin, as she tilted her pretty head towards the weak sun.

"But my dear, have you forgotten the icy fingers of Jack Frost round your throat? Last winter, I thought the battle was lost and I'm not an old goat. It's the cold, I dread and I'm so old, next spring

I could be dead!"

"Calm yourself, old man, and make a plan. Can't you be like me and withdraw your sap into your roots which meet down at your feet? Take a nice long rest. That is for the best," said the Ornamental Oak creaking his big limbs into place."

"My friend, this cannot be for me. You see I'm not a deciduous tree. Through winter, I keep my needles bright and green because I'm the oldest conifer type you will have seen. But this year though I am sage, I am wise. I am feeling my very great age and winter is near I fear."

The Yew drew his branches round him like a cloak until they were touching the ground. A tiny Jenny Wren flew to hide underneath them and keep him company.

It was late autumn in the garden and the smoky smell of dying vegetation was in the air. Most of the flowers in the borders had become dry and dull, their stalks like sticks and their heads rattling seed pods. The leaves which had been red and yellow and purple had been drained to dark brown like tea leaves at the bottom of a drain. The buzzing of insects was no more, and though some birds still sang, there was sadness in their songs and many of their companions had departed to warmer lands.

Occasionally, there was a sound of wild honking and high above a V-shape of geese flew over casting a shadow in the pond. The last of the frog family leapt into the water with a splash and swam under the juniper bush to settle for the long sleep away from the piercing eyes of the heron. The wind had an edge of cold steel. The sun's rays moved further and further away from parts of the garden leaving areas dank and gloomy. Some of the piles of leaves became slimy and stuck to the soil.

If one listened carefully, it was possible to hear a sigh as the plants and the bushes and the trees wished each other a good sleep and pleasant dreams though a few were still wide awake like the hollies who were still producing berries and cheering each other up. Winter was on its way.

Winter arrived with a terrible, silent, magical force. Overnight, the garden was drained of colour. Frost gripped the skeletons of plants bending them into weird forms, painting them white and black. The earth was beaten and beaten until it was so hard it cracked underfoot, and the roots were trapped in the icy depths, unable to move. The bare arms of the deciduous trees stuck out into the sky like witches' fingers, each painted silver white at the end. The garden was still and quiet like a frozen picture in a glass mirror.

The first flakes fell gently, softly, briefly balancing, like feathers on the wood of the branches, but then becoming faster and faster, whirling like a great cloud of goose down in the air until everything was obscured in a duvet of white. It continued to fall like this for days and even weeks. Sometimes the North Wind came to chase the flakes from the trees, and also to pile the snow in huge drifts in different parts of the garden.

Sometimes the sun came to sparkle on the white and melt the particles of ice until they fell a few drops at a time from the black branches. Every night, the frost returned to do his worst, and long icicles formed like gleaming daggers. The garden was completely buried in snow so that it was impossible to discern the separate bushes, trees and plants now that they were lumps under the blanket. The branches creaked and groaned and bent under the weight sweeping them down to the ground. Many broke because the snow was too heavy.

When the thaw came, they emerged black and stained, damp and damaged. The Yew was particularly affected. The centre was all rotten and the outer branches lay lifeless on the ground.

Spring came as it must at the appointed time and the garden awoke. The plants were joyful.

"Spring has sprung, and I can feel a sticky bud on my tongue," shouted the Chestnut.

"My catkins are driving me wild. I feel just like a child," screamed the Willow.

"At my toes, I've a yellow primrose," said the Beech. "But what has happened to the Yew? He should be here too."

They looked, and they looked but where the proud old Yew had stood was only a heap of black needle leaves and crushed branches. They were all very sad because they had been fond of the old man and valued his wisdom, and, though he had predicted his death, they had not expected it. They were all very subdued as they remembered him.

"We must never forget he would always bend a branch to a friend," said the Rose. The others nodded in the breeze.

As they waited and watched and hoped for a sign of life from the old trunk, an amazing thing happened. One morning there was a circle of little green shoots round the black centre and slowly, slowly these grew into tiny new yew trees. The gardeners came to cut out the centre and replant some of these in different parts of the garden where they grew and flourished.

The Snow House

I shall build a castle of snow,
And lie under porous layers
Between the crisp white sheets.

Apart from the world,
I drift under soft covers.
Feel warmth under frozenness.

The silence of snow smothers me.
I taste the clarity of those crystals,
Cower from the exposure of cold light.

The isolation oppresses.
I struggle to survive,
In this igloo of life,
My snow castle.

An Afternoon Tea Party

I'm fair boilin'; ragin' even!" she said out loud and jammed her sandal into the lump of granite that jagged up out of the path. The pain jarred up her bare leg causing her eyes to smart and start to water again but she felt a sense of satisfaction.

"They lied to me," she thought. "An' I'm fair boilin'."

She thought that she liked this expression which she had heard Mrs McGregor use when she was complaining to Mr McGregor about the newspapers that had not been delivered. "Who do they think they are? Jist because they have to come a distance. This may be a wee place, but we have a big order for the Glasgow Herald in this shop and a promise is a promise is it not, Mr McGregor? I'm fair boilin', so I am."

Yes, a promise was a promise and should be kept – besides, she liked the thought of the boiling, all red and sticky like jam. She felt fury in her chest, and her cheeks, too, felt like the sugary strawberries in the pot. Her hair felt heavy and mouldy with heat and the Kirby grip, which was supposed to anchor it, was burning. She imagined it brilliant and molten, like one of the ingots in Daddy's factory at home or one of the branding irons they used on the sheep. Ugh! She remembered the smell of the singed wool choking her nostrils and imagined her own hair smelt charred like the ewes. Yuk, Oh yuk! Maybe if she loosened the belt of her navy-blue serge shorts another knot, she could flap her aertex shirt a little to give her chest some air. Mummy said it was good to give your body some air, but that was when they were on the beach. Well anyway, she didn't care what Mummy said. Never again!

The wool of the shorts was scratchy against her legs, but she liked them. They were just like the ones George wore in The Famous

Five books and she was always solving mysteries and climbing trees and doing exciting things. It was too hot to climb trees, today.

She sighed and hitched her satchel further up her shoulder. The hottest August in Scotland for fifty (or was it a hundred?) years, that was what Daddy had read out of the newspaper. There were forest fires and even some of the heather was black like skeleton sticks, prehistoric fossil plants the colour of her black wax crayon. She had seen fossil plants in the Arthur Mee encyclopaedia that she was only allowed to read when she was ill and her hands were clean. She liked the word 'prehistoric', rolling it round in her mouth like a toffee. She felt rather pleased as she remembered this. Anyway, there were lots of notices in the roads saying 'Beware of Fire' and about not throwing cigarettes from cars and sometimes you could smell acrid pine in the air. She looked up to the mauve curtain of mountains shimmering in the heat of the afternoon. No, she could not see any drifts of smoke coming off the hills, today.

"A perfect afternoon for a picnic is it not?"

That was what Kirsty McDougall said as she packed egg sandwiches into a square of greaseproof paper. "You'll have fun with your friends."

She nearly told Kirsty, then, as the tears formed hot needles in her eyes, but it was too risky because Kirsty would be sure to tell Mummy and there would be a fuss. Anyway, they didn't deserve to know. They were liars. She liked Kirsty McDougall with her apron smell like newly baked scones and her soft Highland speech. What was it Mummy called her? 'Our general factotum.' It seemed a funny word. She heard Mummy telling the other ladies, 'Our general factotum is a local girl and actually rather good.'

Kirsty is good, she thought, 'She cooks for us and dusts and tidies my room and she's my friend.' She remembered the time that she heard the scratching at her bedroom window and woke from a

59

dream when a red devil landed on her bed and flew onto the floor before scrambling back into the night. How she had screamed, and everyone came running! They soothed her and told her it was just a nasty nightmare. But Kirsty was the one who believed her and cuddled her in soft soapy arms until she'd stopped shaking. It was Kirsty who pointed to the big fir tree with branches that swept the eaves near the open skylight and they watched the squirrel, pretty in the daylight, scamper up the trunk and swing from branch to branch, sending out an eerie chatter.

Now she was on the bridge where they played pooh sticks. She allowed herself one look back just to make sure they were not watching, squinting into the sun at the little group of houses scattered like grazing sheep on the edge of the village. Her house was bigger than the other two, with the garden surrounded by a fence, and the others crouched into the dried-out bog. Nobody. The windows gazed back, sightless.

She turned to look at the thin stream of water trickling below. There was hardly any water left in the burns this year. With the sound of their giggles still gurgling in her ears, she imagined drowning the mirror images of their faces and smirks in the brown liquid. Daddy had told her that the water here was acid because it came from peat and that was why the water tasted nice. She didn't want it to taste nice. She wanted it to be horrible, like that murder story she found at the back of the bookcase where the man put his wife in a bath of acid. She wasn't sure exactly what it had done but she knew it had killed her. She screwed up her lips as she tasted bitterness in her mouth. She wanted to kill Mhairi, and Angela; with her long fair plaits,

"I'm called Angela because I'm Daddy's little angel."

Angela, the newcomer, who had come here on holiday for the first time. She hated her!

Mhairi lived here with her grandparents so she always played with Mhairi in the holiday. Mummy said they were inseparable. 'That means we were always together,' she thought, proudly. Then snooty Angela had come and spoiled it. She was so nice at first, sucking up to them both, offering to lend them her annuals, bringing extra liquorice straps and sherbet dabs from the shop, inviting them to come to the sheepdog trials in her Daddy's posh car. They had ice lollies and he didn't seem to mind the red juice running down their chins onto the leather seats.

'Two's a pair, three's a crowd'. She should have listened to Kirsty McDougall. So-what if Mhairi was two years older and Angela was the same age as Mhairi? She might be younger, but she had read lots of books.

Anyway, she was the one who suggested they form a secret society and she was the one who knew about making up codes and passwords and solving clues, so it was only right that she should be leader. She liked the name she had chosen: The Terrible Three. Of course, Famous or Fabulous would have been better, but you needed four or five for that and 'terrible' sounded clever and powerful all at once. Much better than The Three Musketeers which Angela had wanted just because her Daddy suggested it. Angela had never even heard of the book.

She thought that was what had started it. They were all hot and bothered, trying to hatch a plan in the front room of Angela's house this morning and, of course, Angela said she was the oldest and she should choose, and silly Mhairi sided with her. Well Mhairi didn't have too many books in her house so she didn't know much but she didn't need to do that. The memory of Angela's hoity-toity voice ran in her head.

"We know something you don't Miss Know-all! At Christmas, it's your parents. You're stupid. You're a baby. Baby, Baby!"

She shook her head, like a fairground puppet, trying to shake out the shame and anger.

With her fierce movement, she became aware that the boy was still, and was standing just a little way from the bridge. He was looking into the water with his back half turned from her. She knew who he was, of course. She had seen him earlier that morning in the shop. He was with his mother and she had seen Mummy's face go tight and polite when she wished them 'good day.' They had never been here in previous summers. She had heard Kirsty McDougall say they kept themselves to themselves and Mummy say that they weren't quite class, whatever that meant. She just thought they were a bit strange.

Then the tinkers came into the shop because they always came for the Games and made a fair around the field. It was exciting, though she could tell Mummy was cross because she held her hand really tight when the tinker lady placed a crinkled finger on her arm and said she was a bonny wee one with luck in her eyes and Mummy should bring her to have her fortune told. And Mummy gave that smile that didn't reach her eyes and took her out of the shop.

The scrawny boy never talked to anyone. She didn't want to speak to him now, but Mummy said you shouldn't be rude. She thought he hadn't seen her, but as she made her way up the heathery path, she thought she felt his shadow on her back.

She stopped to listen but there was only the satisfied hum of millions of bees and that strange coughing noise that the pheasants made in the wood. She consulted her map which was on a page of jotter. It had taken her ages to colour in all the things. Great wood to the left, third gorse bush to the right, by mossy stone then, keep right on to sunset. This meant west. She was rather pleased with her efforts. Too bad the others couldn't make maps. 'And I found the place,' she thought.

She jumped off onto the springy heather roots, among the feathers of bracken which grew higher than her head and smelt of old sheep and followed the sheep droppings until the ground fell away in a saucer under a gnarled Scots pine. 'Follow, follow, follow! Follow the yellow brick road." Her own humming made her feel better. This was the perfect den. No one could see her.

She reached into the peaty depths of the root for the sharp edges of the biscuit tin. The contents were just as she had left them; the chipped doll's tea-set, the rusty knife she had borrowed without permission. She took the napkin out of her satchel and spread it on a clump of heather. Then she laid out the sandwiches on a dolly tea plate. The edges looked like paper fringes. She drew out a squashed parcel in blue and silver foil with Cadbury's written on the top and tried to cut it into little squares on the tin lid. Ugh! Disgusting! It looked like dog's doings melting in the sun. She poked for her grubby hankie in her pocket and smeared brown stains onto it, then licked her fingers.

A scrabbling noise in the bracken startled her. The boy appeared, looking hot with his shirt hanging out of his tattered khaki shorts.

"Oh, it's you!" she said, and remembering what Mummy said at tea parties. "How do you do? Do sit down. Would you like a cup of tea?"

"Aye." The boy didn't introduce himself but accepted the cup and saucer.

"It's only orange squash. I'm not allowed to make real tea." She felt ashamed.

"A've got matches," he said, taking a small purple box from his pocket.

"Well you shouldn't. It's not allowed."

She used her prim voice. But curiosity got the better of her. Once,

63

when candles were being lit on her birthday cake, she had been allowed to strike the match and blow it out. That had been from a yellow box. Mummy always said that matches are dangerous. She reached for the box, slid it open and pulled out a match. Listening to the scratching noise it made along the side, she felt a bit nervous, then remembered that she didn't care anymore what Mummy said. There was a hiss and she jumped back in surprise as the hot smoking end flew off. Without a word, he took the box from her, struck another match and shook his hand to put out the flame. He handed back the box.

"I'll do it this time," she said, her prim voice now forgotten. 'I'll show them! I am not a baby!' She was tremendously excited about telling Mhairi and Angela of the adventure with her new friend who was guiding her hand along the match box. Neither noticed the curling smoke and flicker of flame growing along the heather bank behind them.

Bordeaux Mixture

"Sur le pont d'Avignon, On y danse, On y danse".

The childhood jingle repeated and repeated itself in her head as she stood watching the river flow past, a dirty brown pattern of waves under a steel grey sky.

Except this is not Avignon and it is far from jolly, she thought, as she pulled her wool coat closer around her body, touching the warm fur of the collar with her chin and adjusting the hat to combat the January wind blowing over the marshes of the Medoc.

Really, she wondered, was it any warmer here in Bordeaux than in Scotland? Well she hadn't come here for the weather.

There were days like today when she had to force herself to leave the warmth of her elegant apartment overlooking the park. She loved the solid wood door that sighed as she shut out the world, the curved staircase with its decorative ironwork, her red velvet chaise-longue and purple silk cushions in the drawing room with its tall windows. From these she watched the children ride the carousel, their bright polished faces matching the painted horses, the ladies dragging their poodles, and the young lovers, bodies entwined under the trees – ah, the lovers!

But one had to go out to the market or, as today, for a constitutional. Daddy always said it was important to take a walk every day for one's health. What did he know? She smiled as she remembered him with his hat and stick sallying forth to buy his cigarettes in the village.

She had made herself walk through the avenue of the park that was once a royal garden, and then through the narrow, cobbled streets of the Chartrons, with the high gabled wine merchant houses that had become so trendy. Now here she was on the draughty quay, with the designer warehouses on one side and the river on the other. Upstream stood the great stone bridge that had brought that song jangling into her head.

Beyond the bridge, a crane poked a black line into the sky and hanging from it was some sort of white bundle, swinging to-and-fro, to-and-fro. She felt her own head copying the motion, swinging to-and-fro above her fur collar and then it came – dreadful, inevitable – the shudder, then the beast inside, clawing at her chest, the pain causing her to crunch in on herself and hold on, hold on.

"Pardon, Madame?"

The boy on roller blades slid deftly by and raced towards his mother at the end of the quay, letting out a scream of exhilarated laughter.

She straightened her body. The pain settled into a dull ache in her stomach, and a gnawing, sad, sense of being alone. All would have been so different if the wee one had been able to struggle from darkness to light. She'd never even seen him, she'd been so ill. He alone had and what use was that. Time was no healer. How old was that boy? Ten, perhaps? She would have liked a boy like that.

With a rattle, a tram rushed passed on the lines across the boulevard and brought back the present. She resumed her walk. Being alone and being lonely are different, she told herself, and it was her choice. Madame Le Brun, who sold her the house, was always asking her for aperitifs. She went once not to be rude and was introduced to her neighbours – an abominable ancient patrician man with a permanent sneer and a tobacco cough and the professional couple on a tight schedule to pick up their children from the grandparents. They weren't interested in her and she was not interested in them.

She wished Madame Le Brun had consulted her before broadcasting her arrival to the Franglais. The persistent Mrs Lawcroft had not stopped calling ever since – so full of brightness and how much she would enjoy their boozy Burns supper.

"Oh Marion you're the real thing. You can recite some Scottish poetry for us. I can promise you it's a real treat. Our organisation is so friendly. You won't be on your own."

But, that was precisely what she wanted – to be left alone.

The worst thing was that all the expats seemed to speak quite fluent French, but with awful flat English vowels and harsh consonants. Immediately she thought this she felt guilty. It was different for her. She had a French grandmother and studied French at University, researched medieval French literature and then taught. She didn't want to become part of their group.

She liked the refinement of Bordeaux, the spare classical Napoleonic architecture and how this contrasted with the overbearing Victorian mansion that she had sold in Glasgow. Everything would be alright if they just left her alone. The voices of her friends jabbed in her head.

"Marion, you can't. What about work? Too soon! Cut yourself off? How can you live? Too soon!

She had been tired of teaching though no one understood this, of course. They just thought it was a reaction. She gave a bleak laugh... a reaction to life? She had to get away. She had to go!

A thin watered-down sun penetrated the clouds, making the scene seem more like a Flemish landscape painting than a southern sky. She decided to continue her walk along the promenade back towards the city to the perfect semicircle of the royal buildings whose symmetry never ceased to give her pleasure. She would look at the curtain of interesting buildings strung out along the river and avert her eyes from the water and the crane.

When she stopped at the open square to look at the monstrous victory fountain where Neptune rode stone horses gilded with ice, a large crow dropped onto the path beside her. He regarded her with black expectant eyes until she clapped gloved hands and he flapped away in a flurry of cawing. What did that mean? Was it a portent?

Enough! She blinked away the sting in her eyes. It was only a bird looking for crumbs. You can go mad you know in these circumstances!

But she was managing. Yes, there were bad head-under-the-coverlet days, but her funds were better than expected. She could afford to live in her beautiful flat and her needs were not great. She could buy cheese, saucisson and bread and open a bottle of good wine, though that could be a mistake. The demons might lurk in the dregs. She slept, but the dreams often came and shortly thereafter sleep ended though the nightmare went on.

She was suddenly conscious of her bones becoming heavy with cold and her nose was pinched. She would strike off into the narrow alleys of the old town and find her favourite café. Perhaps he would be there? Her straying eyes had marked him out one day when she was staring in her usual state, the beautiful young man. She liked his aesthetic cheek bones, the way his thick brown hair flopped over his forehead. She liked watching the way his lean fingers twisted a strand as he bent his head over his book or laptop. He seemed to use the café for work, a cup of cooling café crème by his side. He was very young. He reminded her, reminded her? Push it away. Don't remember. Don't ...!

The café was situated in a cobbled square within sight of a great Romanesque church that stood austere, dwarfing the figures that drifted in and out of its gigantic portals. The café was traditional yet modern, a chequerboard of tiles, a marble topped bar, old wood scuffed tables, lamps of coloured glass, the odd potted palm, and waiters in long aprons. She opened the door, and it welcomed her like her warm blanket of childhood. The scent of roasted coffee beans and buttery pastries assailed her nostrils. It was busy, full of hard, bright conversation. Every table seemed busy. Searching for a seat, she saw him near the window, and there at his table was the only free chair. She tried a feeble "Non" as the waiter steered her there – after all, her pleasure was to observe him from afar – but any resistance was in vain.

"Excusez moi." He raised his head from the computer and regarded her with soft hazel eyes above an aquiline nose, like a benign eagle, she thought, but his mouth was rather feminine, the lips slightly pronounced and puckered.

What did he see? A well preserved but wan woman, quite stylish in her dress (the influence of her French grandmother –clothes were an important statement of survival) but middle-aged, anonymous in his sphere.

"You are welcome, Madame. Please join me. I will just move my books for you."

She was discomfited. His English was impeccable, and it was unusual for someone to identify her nationality so quickly. She hoped he would immerse himself in study again and indeed he did return to his screen while she ordered but then he addressed her.

"You are English Madame. Are you visiting Bordeaux? Ah what do you think of her? Is she not a beautiful city?"

She felt her body tense, withdrawing and responded with a tight reply, "I am not English but Scottish. I now live in Bordeaux."

He did not seem rebuffed, "Ah Scotland, land of lakes and whisky and kilts and Walter Scott, I am going there, next year when I finish

69

my degree. I will study for a Masters at Strathclyde University. Perhaps you can advise me about the culture? I hear the Scots are a very friendly nation, but when they drink a beer they become angry, so it is necessary to be careful."

Despite her reserve, she found herself drawn into the conversation. He was studying social economics, but he liked literature, particularly English literature which he had studied since primary school. His parents lived abroad most of the time, he said vaguely. He stayed at the flat of an aunt, but he hardly saw her. He was writing a project. Perhaps she would like to hear about it?

If he noticed her reluctance to give any information about herself, he gave no sign, gliding from one topic to another in a way that was entirely engaging. His eyes appraised her face with total attention.

For the first time in months, perhaps longer, she felt interesting, appreciated, somehow just a little alluring; a slight moist pinkness suffused her skin. When she got up to go to the cloakroom, his eyes followed her and when she returned she was conscious of them searching, smiling her back to her seat. He was full of enthusiasm for his city and when, almost reluctantly, she drew her coat round her to take her leave, he leaned forward and placed a hand on her arm so that she could feel the warmth of his fingers through the tweed.

"There is an interesting exhibition of photographs at the Musee. Would you let me show it to you? It costs less on Tuesday. I propose we meet in the hall at twelve, after my class. Please agree. It would be my pleasure. My name is Pierre Le Bac, by the way. What is yours?"

"Marianne", she said. And so it began.

As she waited in the big hall of the museum, she hid herself behind one of the pillars. This is ridiculous. I was not going to come, had no intention of coming. Her pulse was going too fast. Oh you stupid woman! And there he was, his eyes raking the atrium, a slight boy, clad in tight black jeans and a faded leather jacket.

When he saw her, his smile caressed her in an unfamiliar way that made her heart jump inside her chest. He kissed both cheeks in a formal yet informal way and as they proceeded to the softly lit depths of the gallery, his hand brushed hers as he indicated the way to the photographic exhibition.

She watched fascinated as he expounded on the merits of the photographs which captured the social history of the Landes. His eyes burned like the forest fires in the sepia frames. She gazed mesmerized by the endless shots of thirty's' brides and grooms, grinning, bashful, full of hope, flanked by reams of relatives, into a desolate future in a long ago past. They had nothing to do with her. She listened to his theories as if they were profound.

Afterwards, he took her through the main collections, and she was as delighted by his knowledge of the early history, the Roman artefacts of Bordeaux, the teeming medieval streets and the religious statues as he was by her appreciation of his knowledge. He guided her upstairs to see the navigation models and they both stared in sympathetic silence at the depictions of the slave trade. When he touched her shoulder, she did not shrink away.

She had paid the entrance fee, but she felt she should offer him a drink. They went to a local bar where they talked and talked until she felt the need to go home and she realised for those hours she had not thought of anything but the present. The present was everything, for now.

It became an established pattern. Every Tuesday, they went to a gallery or they walked and talked, if the weather permitted. He took her to the gallery of modern art where the bizarre colours of the installations contrasted with the grey incessant rain of the outside world. He insisted they climb to the top of the house of perilous chairs and dance to the music of an old jukebox below. He called her queen of the chairs and presented her with a tulip picked from a civic bed. He took her hand and made her run over the bridge with the wind grabbing their hair until they were breathless and exhilarated. She heard the strange sound that was her own laughter and wanted to reach out and touch it.

He said, "Marianne, you are even more beautiful when you laugh."

Crazy, crazy, but where was the harm? They were just playing, he and she. Perhaps there was some kudos in being with an older woman? She still found it difficult to sleep but now she found, sometimes, a younger face disturbed her dreams and she began to look forward just a little.

In those early days, he was considerate, solicitous always of her welfare, a hand under her arm on slippery cobbles, holding the umbrella above her head, asking what would interest her, how she felt, complimenting her dress, noticing anything new. He appeared happy and drew her into his mood. He had the enthusiasm of youth. He was witty and charming. Gradually her frozen veins began to thaw.

She checked him on Google of course but, to her surprise, there was no more information than his University registration, no pictures of smiling student friends on Facebook. She never gave him her surname and she always turned in another direction so that he would not guess where she lived. He never asked. Only once, he said, "Marianne, you live alone?" She did not reply but she knew he knew.

The centre of Bordeaux is a small place and although she had few acquaintances, she wondered that they never met someone he knew. Once, on another weekday, when she walked past a café near the University, she did see him with a group of students, shivering under the blue heaters in the street. He was drawing on one of the long black cigarettes which he loved and gesticulating to a group of giggling girls with long sleek hair and impossibly short skirts showing thighs, tight and narrow, in leggings above long boots.

She found it impossible not to watch, the long forgotten unfamiliar pain of jealousy stirred her. She wanted to kill those girls, to kill him! He saw her standing there, detached himself from the group and rushed forward to seize her arm. She was the only one who mattered in that moment.

He liked music. For a treat she arranged tickets for the opera in the grand theatre. As they strolled arm in arm at the interval in the salon, admiring the classical cherubs, a hand tapped her back and the flat tones of Anne Lawcroft rang out,

"Well Marion, fancy seeing you here. We were beginning to think you never went out. And is the lad here, your nephew? Introducing him to the sights of Bordeaux, are you?"

Either she was malicious or stupid. She must have seen he was French.

Looking back, Marion could not remember which came first, the fluctuations in his moods, the sex, or the requests for financial help. Of course, she could remember the first time they went to a seedy little hotel where she hired a room. By that time the urgency of need had become desperate for her in a way she would not have believed. He suggested it tentatively, only if she felt ready. He knew she did not want to take him home. That was never considered, and his aunt's house was in a suburb. It would be impossible. His lovemaking was rough and gentle by turns. Satisfying. He praised her body though she could feel the tautness of her stomach loose with age. After, he fell asleep while she watched the rise and fall of his down covered chest.

There was a day when they went for a trip down the river. The early spring sun was warm on their faces and the boat was full of noisy children. He seemed tetchy and complaining then lapsed into sullen silence when she told him he was being intolerant. Later, he told her he was worried because his aunt was looking for more rent and his parents could not be contacted. She offered him thirty euros as a small loan and he was delighted. The amounts increased though she kept an account and he promised he would be able to pay back when he had a job in the summer. She didn't care. Perhaps it was right that she should pay for the sex which continued to be good.

On other occasions, his mood seemed almost manic with happiness and energy and he would shriek with laughter at any little witticism. Once she saw him when she was walking home rather late through the old town though he had warned her that the streets could be dangerous at night. He was talking to a man at the back of a dark close and they were arguing she could see. She didn't mention it. Her ring went missing, the diamond and sapphire one she had inherited from her mother and which he often admired. He sympathised. It was loose on her finger and she had meant to have it taken in. Perhaps she could claim it on the insurance? He asked her for a large sum of money to pay tuition fees and she found herself refusing.

It happened late in the evening as the May dusk was slipping into night. She was preparing for bed, when there was a great beating at the door and it was him. He was distressed, crazy with emotion, appeared scared of something, streaks of sweat and blood on his face. He said his aunt had turned him out. He thought he could stay at a friend's in the Moroccan quarter, but he had been attacked in the street by a gang of youths. He said he knew where she lived because he had once followed her. She wasn't sure. It was a new phenomenon, his presence in her house, but things had gone too far.

He came to her bed as they both knew he would. In the night she rose silently not to waken him and went to her bathroom where his clothes lay scattered on the floor. On instinct, she emptied the pockets of his jerkin and her hand extracted the paper with the white powder, and she knew. Suddenly, all the anger about the other welled up within her like molten lava and she was in the bedroom screaming and hitting his head with a heavy book, scratching his eyes with her nails, tearing at his body. He ran out of the flat half naked. She waited until late morning before she reported the loss of her credit card.

Of course, he wasn't there when she visited the café the next Tuesday. She stirred the brown liquid of the coffee until it made little waves like the Gironde.

"Sur le pont d'Avignon. On y danse, On y danse"

Bordeaux January

Skeletons of Christmas trees line cobbles stained with white.
Grey shutters, closed on elegant windows, conceal separate lives.
Click clack! Hurrying heels ring on frost-dead paving stones.
A gilt ball swings from the still dense green bough above the
   Boulangerie,
As a customer enters with a last request to recapture departed joy,
In the form of a Gallette du Roi.

Recaptured dead manikins hang from walls of garish yellow.
Climb the house of stacked chairs and you will reach the blue
   heaven.
On screen, a red man extols the Disney dreams of desert city.
A hammock strung from balconies swings; a kaleidoscope, pink
   and white.
Outside the museé warehouse, the constant rain mutters
A dirge of grey sludge in the gutters.

Star of Wonder

'In the bleak midwinter, frosty wind made moan.' The voices of the Salvation Army carol singers outside Woolworths sounded awfy thin and cold, jist like the weather, she thought, as she rubbed at a dark spot on the shelf where some oil had been spilt. The brown looked just like the piles of Demerara sugar slush melting on the pavement. She gave up and rearranged a piece of tinsel to cover the place. Mr MacGregor was that fussy, but he was busy in the back of the shop.

She sniffed, but the end of her nose had no real feeling in it and she was scared that a wee cold drop was forming. 'I couldnae thole to be like auld Aggie wi her dreeping nose.' She dived into the pocket of her overall for her hankie and dabbed hastily. What must it be like to have nane, only an empty hole – to be like that man in an iron mask. She had heard a story on the radio. She shuddered. Her nose was not her best feature; she knew this – too long with a wee dent at the top like a humpbacked bridge where the ball flung by that skellum next door had broken it. The tip had a tendency to turn yeasty pink, like uncooked ham.

'Rudolph the red nosed reindeer had a very shiny nose.' The choir was singing, more lustily this time. Tears pricked her eyes with wee jags as she remembered her schoolmates singing the same words all too often.

"Dinnae greet, hen! They're jist jealous because they dinnae have nice eyes and a good skin like you." It had been true. She had nae plooks on her face when theirs had looked like one of those pictures of a volcanic landscape that you found in copies of the National Geographic magazine in Dr McKay's waiting room.

She sniffed again, just to remind herself of the existence of her nose. She smelled the sharp yet sweet smog of paraffin from the one heater in the corner mixed with the other scents of the shop; wax, resin and metal, earthy wood and bulb fibre, penetrating cleaning fluids, Jeyes, Silvo, Brasso, green scrubbing soap and the warm heather honey of wood polish. The smell of the heater was overpowering, and it scarcely took the chill off, but she had always liked the other scents of the ironmonger's shop.

Even as a wean wi her hand clutched in Mam's she had liked the whiff from it better than the liquorice, aniseed and sherbet of the sweetie shop. She had been that pleased when Mr MacGregor had said that she could have the assistant's job. She had been jist bursting to run hame and tell Mam.

"That's good hen. I'm awfy proud. You've got a secure job not like that ne'er-do-well laddie of Maimie's. I heard Will Scott got the sack from Milne's again for his timekeeping. Pair Maimie's beside hersel!"

She had been glad for herself. It was true that now she had been in the shop for a year, Mr MacGregor did trust her and sometimes, like now, he left her in charge. Still, she was sorry about Will Scott. He wisnae a bad lad.

The prickly heat began to rise under the neck of her cardigan, the one Mam had knitted for her last Christmas, as she remembered.

It was the night of the school Christmas dance and the hall which stank of gym shoes, bodies and stale chips had been festooned with garlands of paper bells. Irn Bru orange, crocodile green and that weird witch purple swung above the Christmas tree fairy, reaching for escape into the ropes and beams hanging from the ceiling.

A tinny record-player behind the piano in the corner was belting out 'Jimmy Shand and his Band' music for the reels and country dances which they had been learning for the last few weeks. She had been wearing her new dress with the sticky-out skirt over a petticoat like a meringue, and a top that clung a little to her newly formed breasts that felt too heavy for her ribcage. These were concealed under her powder-blue angora cardigan.

She had been excited before the dance but, once there, she clung to the walls, sitting with her head down, wanting to dance, but terrified she would be asked to. A few of the male teachers doing their duty had approached her, but she hung her head and blushed so much that few had insisted. Only once, her gym teacher, Mrs McColl, had pushed her into a Paul Jones.

It was the second-last dance, a St Bernard waltz, when a big red hand was thrust at her. A gruff question followed. "You dancin?" She looked up a long way and saw his eyes, hazel wi flecks like woven tweed, soft, maybe kind, in his big bony face under his sharp, slicked attempt at a crew cut. Will Scott lived in the same tenement, older than her a bit so she didn't really know him because they hadn't played in the stair at the same time.

She had let him guide her onto the floor and place a damp hand just below her bra line. At first, she had been embarrassed, awkward in her moves, but she knew her steps and she let the music carry her. After a wee while, it had seemed she was dancing in a dwam. The music stopped and started again and then he was leading her back to her wall.

"Ta very much. You're no' a bad wee dancer, hen." He slouched off.

She couldn't see him among the close birling couples crowding the floor for the last dance, and then she was dragged into the big circle for Auld Lang Sang and the cheers. Later among the pegs of the girls' cloakroom as she was buttoning her warm coat, Jessie Souter stuck her head through the railings.

"Ah saw you with that big loon, Wullie Scott. You were well away wi' it. You better watch yersel, hen. He's trouble!" She hadn't responded, and the poking face was withdrawn. She had hurried out into the dark night. However, as she had turned out of the school gates, she was aware of a presence stepping out of the shadows and the rasp of his voice,

"Gaen hame braw wee dancer? Ah'll get you along the road, then." She nodded, and they fell into step though she had to almost run to follow his loping stride, little curls of their breath like wisps of cloud in the frosty air. After a while she had asked; proud, indignant, happy,

"Wiz yah waiting for me?"

"Aye, maybe hen."

It was not far, and that had been their only conversation. When they reached the tall buildings with the Christmas trees bleezing with lights in the windows, he had suddenly reached for her hand and said, "Let's go round the back," and she let him guide her to the backend of the close where they ducked through into the darkness of the drying green with its web of wash lines and the black shapes of the cludgie doors.

It was here she felt the warmth of his arms surrounding her shivering body and his breath on her skin as he reached his face down to hers, his lips rough but sweet on hers, and then his tongue pushing further and curling round hers until she had no breath left. She knew his fingers were searching, moving on the wool of her coat where her breasts were round, and his body seemed hard and knobbly as he pressed her against the wall. She had been scared but excited at the same time.

Then suddenly he had released her.

"Never been kissed afore hen?" Gentle, he led her to the backdoor and gave her a wee push. "Well you're awe right, hen. You're a guid wee kisser an awe! See you!"

And that was it. She had scarcely seen him again, only as a figure in the distance. He left the school first and she only knew about his jobs and his wildness from things Mam said. She shivered. He was her wee secret!

The shop bell gave a loud tinkle and the door opened to let in a cold blast of 'Once in Royal David's city' and a large lady in a fur with a pudding-basin hat entered.

"Good afternoon, Mrs Bell. How can I be of help?" She clasped her cold hands tight together under the counter. She didn't like the woman – she was that fierce and snobby – but this shop-assistant was well-trained.

"Oh! I ... it's you. I was hoping for some professional advice from Mr MacGregor, but if he's not here I suppose you'll do. I need a big pan for my New Year turkey. There'll be eighteen, so it'll be a big bird."

She recognised that she should be impressed by this information. She also knew that Mrs Bell would leave the shop a dissatisfied customer if she settled for a pan which was less than adequate but might jist do a turn. Indeed, this was the outcome.

"Now mind and pass on compliments of the season to Mr MacGregor. I didn't see your mother at the Kirk on Sunday. Well I hope her cold improves. That scarf of hers has seen better days. You could do worse than give her a new one for Christmas."

The spirit of the season seemed to strike her. "I have a good few Paisley wool ones, not silk but warm, I have no more need for. I'm sure she would be glad of one. I'll bring it to the next Guild meeting." And she was out the door in a flurry of self-inflicted goodwill and meagre snowflakes which were beginning to fall outside.

"Interfering auld besom! Mam likes her scarf." It had been Da's last present. She sniffed. Nearly closing time!

She wrote the sale in the book slowly and carefully, so it was clear, just as her employer had taught her. He was fussy, but he was kind, and she liked it here. She was glad to have found this job.

It was almost dark outside now and the lights in the shop cast an orange glow on the icy pavement with the wee fluffy flakes dancing like moths against the pane, and dark shapes of people rushing past. The tinsel was all that sparkly way where the light caught it. She smiled. The Sally Ann were still at it. 'Star of Wonder, Star of night, Star of beauty shining bright.'

The shop bell clanged and one of the shapes detached itself from the night and entered, a tall man with a shabby coat and a cloth cap at a jaunty angle. At first, she didn't recognise him. He was awfy thin about the face but his hoarse tones stirred her memory and when she caught his eye, she felt a stream of warm blood coursing up from her frozen toes to her neck.

"Whit are you daen here?"

Surprise made her sharp.

"Well that's not much of a welcome from the braw wee dancer, is it, hen? Ahm on a shoppin trip. Whit have yez got for knives? Ahm after wan for a job. In wi' a chance wi' a jiner."

She didn't believe him. His boots were wrecked, scuffed into holes held together by knots in the laces. There was a sense of urgency, desperation about him that was sad, despite the bravado. Yet something still attracted her to him. She drew out the drawer where the knives lay in a row on the cloth like bodies in a mortuary, each in its coffin indentation. They gleamed and sparkled like stars in the shop light as she began to show Will Scott the selection.

Dryburgh

The green cold from the grey walls
Enters my body like algae, creeping
Under my brown habit of wool, drawn
From sheep grazing under the old trees,
In the policies by the river.
Bleating, innocent, feckless,
All God's creatures.

Infused with ice, I no longer know if I am a man,
The man who came to walk in the ways of God,
In quiet contemplation in a Borders' abbey
Of soaring arches and peaceful piety,
Who shuffled gladly to take offices
Ten times a day.

My frozen bones ache with rheumatism.
The pain, the suffering, is excruciating.
Oh Lord, I am weary of this world!
And yet our waiting was decreed.
The low moan of devotional chants,
Sharp, high shouts of an oyster-catcher.
They torment my ears.

I long for the furnace heat
Of the great "warming room",
The hot gruel dripping warm
Blood into my intestines,
Steaming breath of companions,
And appalling scent of human flesh.
Slow freezing is my penance.
The iron chain clanks heavy.
I try to hold my balance.

The cowl has slipped,
My head exposed.
Did I deserve this fate?
Others felt but did not act.
My challenge was not unwarranted.

The sound of metal thudded in my head.
I tasted iron on my tongue.
He pushed Old Gregory beyond the edge,
That cruel man-made Godhead
In a House of Sanctity, by false authority.

I struck the Abbot with my fist.
My consciousness is sliding into dark,
My limbs dissolving like spring snow.
O Lord, hard I repent my sins.
Even my just anger, strong and black
Like the boughs which sweep the orchard.
Wash it white as the sweet cherry blossom.
Receive my soul in grace!

Those who tread lightly on the grass,
Grey lichen growth on stones do find.
Monuments of eminent folk will pass,
Those who left rich legacies behind.
But think on him who had eschewed all vanity,
And suffered fate dictated by humanity.
He too lies in this sacred plot.
Forget him not?

A Night of Torment

A monologue for radio

(MUSIC: THE NIGHTMARE SONG FROM IOLANTHE)

Of course, I can remember my earliest memory, but I wasn't going to tell that 'nicey, nicey' young man this afternoon. It is in fact a remarkable feat for someone of my age. Yes, my girl, you've always had a remarkable memory.

I must have been about a year, perhaps even less. I was in my pram – one of those high carriage affairs, I suppose. Great dark shades on either side, it was like a cave. Anyway, I remember peering out and a huge face leering at me, dangling outside and making horrible 'ooing' sounds. I opened my lungs and mouth and let them have it. Funny...the memory just cuts out there like a cinematic flash and the lights go out. I still don't like big faces – can't abide cartoons. Those Andy Warhol pictures with screaming colours and distorted features give me the pip!

It was Nanny I presume, since I scarcely recall seeing Mama in my early years and she certainly would not have done anything so vulgar as smiling at a baby. Cooing was definitely de rigour and nonsensical since, in her opinion, there was no point in communicating with babies as they understood nothing. She wasn't interested in her children until they could have an intelligent conversation. She was, after all, an intellectual.

Perhaps it was one of the maids, Violet or Rose. It would have been like them. When I was a little older, I can remember sitting on the rug with the warm wool smell, by the range, playing with my rag doll, Lily, and Mr Wooden Spoon and hearing their clatter and chatter in their funny voices – the chorus of my childhood. And then on one occasion, Mr Wooden Spoon had a great fall. He

85

splintered and Lily was crying fit to burst, and Violet – or was it Rose? came and wound a bandage around Mr Wooden Spoon and pulled me on to her apron with her big, red, chapped hands. She sang, 'Humpty Dumpty sat on a wall. Humpy Dumpty had a great fall. All the king's horses and all the king's men couldn't put Humpty together again.' I thanked her very politely because she had rescued Mr Wooden Spoon and no mistake, and I couldn't understand because they all laughed.

Perhaps that was the beginning of realising that when I meant one thing, the world meant another. I also think I liked my perambulator rather well. It was my kingdom. I've always liked my own space – dreadful If I creak open my eyelids, I can just see the shape of the tallboy. Solid Victorian. Henry insisted. Looks like an upturned coffin. Hmph! The wardrobe with the hatbox on top looks like an undertaker with a chimney hat come to take me away. I'm not dead yet I can tell you! Anyway, they don't wear those things anymore. That young man with a vulture's beak, poke, poking into my past; he thinks you're nearly dead, Daphne. Well, I don't want to think about him. He won't beat me with his biographical notes.

I started plotting from my pushchair. If I pretend I'm a brainy princess, Mama will notice me. If I tell Papa, I went to the Zoo with Mama and a nice uncle, Papa will become really interested in what I have to say.

Oh no! Mr Digging Diggory with your recorder, "Just a minute, Daphne. That's frightfully important." You can't fool me. You can't trap my memories like mice in your little digital box. No, no. I mustn't think about that, or sleep will never come. Modern expression though it is!

(SOUND OF CLOCK STRIKING ONE)

Night is the enemy of sleep. Did I write that? I can't remember.

No sleep for the wicked. Now that's certainly true and I didn't write that. Shall I try another trip down memory lane? Better than the proverbial sheep, but then it didn't work, did it?

Maybe I should remember Henry. Such a decent man but so, soo boring. Life with Henry was regulated by gin and tonic and The Times. It was all 'cross the tees' with Henry: wake up to the tic toc, toast and The Times; take the train – tit tit tee tit tit tee; tiffin at Lyons Corner House; tea and muffins in the drawing room; tonic and a generous gin, but not before the appointed hour; and bed at ten past ten, precisely. A few tentative tender approaches, then time for shut eye followed by his tremendous resounding nasal performance. He snored like a walrus. I should be used to lack of sleep. Apnoea I believe they call it now. A pain to annoy you, I call it. Still, he never interfered with my 'scribbling,' as he called it. He thought he provided stability for my otherwise wayward character. Poor, dear, stupid Henry. He couldn't have stopped me if he had tried with his wet fish ways. Still, he did have an income and the house, and he was awfully handsome when I married him. We were a disappointment to each other. Life's full of disappointments to be tolerated.

(SOUNDS OF WATER IN PIPES)

Rumble, thumble. Old houses talk, don't you know? The plumbing's elderly, creaking in its bones like me. I lie here and I hear the house rustle and flap like a great goose settling its feathers. An arthritic bird, like me, which creaks and rumbles.

(SHORT SILENCE)

I think I'll just have a little nightcap from the bottle that sustains. That's it. Switch on the lamp and have a little glug of my lovely, amber liquid.

(SOUND OF GLASS AND POURING OF LIQUID THEN

SWALLOWING)

No harm once a day at my age but ... silly old codger that doctor! Never believe a word he says. Keep it topped up. Keep it on the bedside table. Beautiful cut glass decanter, the only decent thing father left me. That and his debts.

So much for the matinee idol lookalike grandson of a Marquis-turned-author. He published a few plays, popular for a moment then melted like snow on the tide of public opinion. Well I know what that's like, don't I? That young man all avid and intense,

"But they're unrecognised classics of their time, Daphne."

Really, Mr D. eh what is your name? You must forgive me. At my age etc. etc. You're looking for the story, I thought, and you're not going to get it. Just once, I dropped his name like a little crumb into my teacup of life. The young man's chin nearly fell into his tea. Then, I steered away on a new current of tealeaves and the name sank in an eddy of Darjeeling, unable to resurface.

He was pallid and drawn, that young man when he left. I was triumphant but exhausted. Those secret diggers are all the same, but I hold the faces of trumps in my hand so it's no bid, Mr Diggory! I think that's the reason sleep will not come, tonight.

Exhaustion is a strange emotion. The body is rendered bereft of action but though your brain is drained like a teacup, there's still that drop that swirls round and round in a whirlpool of thought. The moment I close my eyes the pictures are so real. Memory's the thief of sleep! I think I'll have another little snifter to chase away the thoughts.

(SOUND OF GLASS AND DRINKING)

That's better. A warm glow at the back of my throat and gradually, gradually spreading into my bones. Sleep, sleep creeping into my eyes. Time to put out the light.

(BRIEF SILENCE THEN SOUND OF AN OWL)

Arrh! What? Oh it's you my friend, phonetic companion of the wakeful night. OOH OOH! What tiny animal shall be your prey, tonight? They're all hunters, men!

Henry hunted me in his own way and then he hunted a humdrum life until he found it.

That Mr What's-his-name hunting for 'the truth', I suppose he would call it. But it's all a game that men enjoy. Even he who shall not be named was a hunter and I loved him for it.

He was bright and bold like no other and his mind and whole body throbbed with the power of it. I should know. I held him to me. He hunted fame and fortune for his literary prowess and by God, he found it. Yes, men are hunters. Women are sustainers. I was jealous of his intellect and yet I loved it. I published. He published. I knew mine wouldn't last despite some minor acclaim and I knew his would. But I treasured the fact that I was the catalyst for many of his works. Our secret! Our secret! A long time ago until Mr Diggory Dig gets a little whiff, spies an old forgotten scandal of the literary scene and woof, we're off on the trail. Well Mr D ....

(SOUND OF A TRAIN IN THE DISTANCE)

Night mail rushing through the dark. Boom biddee boom, boom biddee boom. None of your Henry's tame tubes. I love express trains. Soot in your nose. Settled in a red upholstered room. Sash windows. Smut in your eye. Scenery rushing by, and oh the excitement of anticipation! Arrival in his arms! I tried the diesels, once or twice. Smelled of dead cat and no privacy.

That was how I met him, on the Brighton line. I was scribbling in a corner and he noticed. I knew who he was, of course. I kept stealing glances under my lashes. I had long lashes then. He enquired about my writing. When the Attendant came we shared tea and scones. Later, we shared a whole lot more.

We travelled everywhere by train, all over Europe. It was the only way to be together in those ridiculously small shaking beds, listening to the rattle of the wheels, stifling my cries in the hard little pillows. I told Henry so many lies, so many fictitious holidays with old school friends: walking in Switzerland with Moira; cruising the Rhine with Caroline; shopping with Stella in Paris. I wonder? I wonder now if he knew and didn't want to know. No holes in the fabric of his life, poor Henry.

I know what he wants of course. He wants the letters, my treasures tied up in faded tape in a drawer and he wants permission to publish. We wrote, of course, all the time – his thoughts were my thoughts – no names, our own code. I told him to destroy mine but he hid them. No fool like an intelligent fool, eh? I thought they had lost interest in the secret lover, those academics. But now he's come, this earnest young man. Funny thing is, he reminds me of myself.

(SHORT SILENCE)

I think I'll just have another little drop.

(SOUNDS OF GLASS AND POURING)

That silly fool of a doctor offered me sleeping pills. Certainly not, I said. Pills are for pillocks! Like you, I nearly added. I don't want to sink to my hereafter on a wave of Prozac! No fuzzy-wuzzy end for me. My intellect's all I've got to keep me in this world.

I went to his funeral in a dowdy grey coat and hid behind a pillar. Such a grand affair. So many people! I needn't have worried.

(MUSIC, LAND OF HOPE AND GLORY BY ELGAR, SHE HUMS)

Ridiculous! Land of Hope and Glory! England's finest! As if he was a patriot. He was a true European, God damn it! He would have laughed. I began to giggle and then I had to slip out with my handkerchief between my teeth. But the gasps of laughter turned to sobs and my whole body was consumed as I clutched the portico because we would never laugh together again.

(MUSIC FADES THEN SILENCE)

The money would be useful, of course. I don't spend much these days, but the little comforts don't come cheap. I like real coffee and good whisky.

"Daphne, never sell yourself cheap," he used to say.

The written word was worth something then. No royalties now. Last time I saw one of my books, it was in the pile of discarded 'take one please' at the library. I suppose I would have a moment of fame. The secret lover exposed. Out, out brief candle! Perhaps they would republish. Those feminist presses are always digging out old authors. Rediscovered genius of the thirties! Dated claptrap! Don't delude yourself, Daphne.

(SOUND OF CATS FIGHTING)

Sounds like the girls in my common room. "OOUGH! Monica, you stole my pen!" "Noo Fiona you dropped ink on my blouse. I'm telling Matron." To be ignored.

I never belonged to their set. I am complete unto myself.

(SOUND OF ONLY ONE CAT MEWLING)

A baby crying? "We were never blessed," Henry used to say. I told him I wasn't interested in children; nasty mewling creatures who mess up your lives. A man who liked order, he could see the point of that. I pretended. It wasn't true. Oh, how I longed for a baby to cradle and love as my parents failed to do. They say you can't parent unless you have been parented well. Nonsense! It welled in my stomach, that great pool of love waiting to gush forth.

Once, I knew I was pregnant. Oh, I had such plans for my son, such deceptions for Henry even for him. Nothing would matter except me and my child. I watched them disappear in an eddy of water and a pool of blood in the washroom of our hotel in Florence. I felt so cold, frozen to death for such a long time. I feel cold now. Draw up the blankets, Daphne. Got to keep living. That young man doesn't want to see a corpse when he comes. Come to think of it, he would be about the same age as my son.

(SOUND OF THE DAWN CHORUS)

At last the dark is beaten into submission by the dawn. I can see sepia light creeping around the blind. "Cheep, cheep" my friends, I love your song. Light comes so early in the spring, says she in the autumn of her life. I remember lying, listening to the dawn chorus glowing with the pleasure of it after attending a ball. I felt so young and fresh with my world before me. The world is for the young, Daphne! I would have liked a child to take my genes and my ideas into posterity. I have no legacy to give.

I haven't read them for years; a bundle of fading parchment gathers dust. It was all a very long time ago, but I have an excellent memory. Well, you can have them, Mr Diggory Dig! And now it's time to sleep.

(MUSIC FROM BEETHOVEN'S PASTORAL AFTER THE STORM)
THE END

Night, Fire, Romance and Fate

A surreal drama with three characters: Fred, Ella and Another

SCENE 1 - NIGHT

Fred: The light's gone out.

Ella: It's terribly dark now. I can't see you, Fred, and I can't see him. It's coal black in here.

Fred: Black as pitch...Pitch black, Ella.

Ella: Black as ink...Inky black, Fred.

Fred: Black, black night, Ella.

Ella: Devilish black, Fred. Why doesn't he say anything? Why don't you say anything? I'm talking to you, you know?

Fred: Perhaps he's asleep, Ella.

Ella: Do you think they'll come, Fred?

Fred: Oh I think they'll come. They'll come alright.

Ella: Maybe they'll come in the morning.

Fred: That's right. Maybe they'll come in the morning.

(PAUSE)

Ella: Fred, I can see a light. See, it's like a spear, a silver spear, cutting the floor like a cake.

Fred: You're dreaming, Ella.

Ella: No really, Fred. I'm going to touch it. See...if I just crawl over as far as that, I can dip my finger in the light.

(SOUND OF CRAWLING)

Ella: Fred?

Fred: What, Ella?

Ella: It's the moon, Fred; a great big silver moon and it's trying to get through the crack in the wall.

Fred: Can't keep a good moon out, Ella.

(PAUSE)

Ella: Would you like to see the moon? Yes you! Fred, I think he should see the moon.

Fred: That's right, Ella. A full moon is magic.

Ella: Shall we try to push him there? Prop him up so he can see the moon? He'll like that. Let's try, Fred.

Fred: Alright, Ella. Altogether now. One, two, three, heave.

(SOUNDS OF HEAVY BREATHING, SHUFFLING, SHOVING, PANTING AND THEN SIGHS)

Ella: That's good, Fred. He can see now. You can see it now, can't you? He's awake, Fred. Let's sing and he can join in.

Fred and Ella (sing)

By the light, (by the light, by the light)

Of the silvery moon, I want to spoon,

To my honey, I'll croon love's tune

Honeymoon, keep a'shining in June,

Your silvery beams, will bring love's dreams,

We'll be cuddling soon,

By the silvery moon.

Fred: It's gone, Ella.

Ella: What's gone, Fred?

Fred: The moon's gone. A big curtain's drawn on the moon and it's black forever night.

SCENE 2 – FIRE

(SOUNDS OF BANGS AND CRACKLES)

Ella: What's that noise, Fred?

Fred: Haven't you heard there's a war on? Go back to sleep, Ella. It's just those monkeys in the sky.

Ella: Fred! Fred! I can see red dancing through this crack. How pretty it is! Flicker, flicker, flash. Flicker, flicker, flash. It's like a chorus of fireflies dancing nearer and nearer. Legs up, bend, flash. Legs down, bend, flicker. Flick...

Fred: Do you smell something? Do you think he...?

Ella: Don't be silly, Fred. He smoked his last some time ago. Puff, puff, puff!

(SINGS)

Puff, the magic dragon lived by the sea...

Fred, I do smell smoke. Nasty, acrid stuff, it hurts my nose. The wall's warm. Fred! I touched the wall and the stone was warm! They wouldn't have would they?

Fred: They would. There's no knowing. We need to move fast, Ella!

Ella: We can't, Fred. What'll we do? Fred ask him what to do? Why doesn't he answer? Why don't you? Don't you?

Fred: Don't pull at him, Ella. Tell you what, his coat's damp. He won't mind if we take it off and roll it up under the door.

(SOUNDS OF HEAVING AND PUSHING MATERIAL)

Fred: That's done it. It won't come now.

Ella: Oh, Fred. He's saved us. He's saved our bacon. Thank you, thank you!

The red light's faded away. I can see through the crack. It's all charred and black.

Fred: Coal black night. (MURMERS) Bloody nearly was our bacon!

SCENE 3 – ROMANCE

Ella: The moon's here again, Fred. I can see it. There's a frost outside; silver frost etched on everything. It's beautiful, eerie and beautiful. The world's really beautiful, Fred, if you look hard enough.

Fred: Moonlight becomes you, Ella. Care for a dance?

Ella: How can we? Besides, what will he think?

Fred: I'll ask him, shall I? Dear Sir, would you mind if this dear lady and I perambulate the floor? Perhaps you would be so kind as to provide some music for this occasion?

(PAUSE)

Ella: Fred, I can't move. You know I can't move.

Fred: No matter, my dear. Take my hand. One hand joined in another. Feel our rhythm permeate your body. Listen to your heartbeat. Listen to my heartbeat. Boom did did dee. Boom did did dee.

(MUSIC - INVITATION TO THE DANCE)

Ella: Oh Fred, that was lovely. I feel so warm and gentled in your arms. I think he liked it too. Didn't you?

Fred: He clapped, Ella, but you didn't hear. Sleep now, Ella before the morrow comes.

SCENE 4 – FATE

(SOUNDS OF TAPPING ON STONE)

Ella: Do you think they're coming, Fred?

Fred: I don't know, Ella. They could be.

Ella: I don't want them to come yet, Fred. I'm scared.

Fred: What will be, will be.

Ella: I don't think that's clever, Fred. This isn't the time for platitudes. You've always liked platitudes and I hate them.

Fred: I think that's a little unfair, Ella. If you hadn't...

(THE KNOCKING BECOMES LOUDER)

Ella: Well, think of something, Fred. What do you think Mr...? I can't remember his name. Fred.

Fred: Well that's alright. Neither can I. He doesn't mind.

Ella: Well what can we...?

Fred: We could join him.

Ella: You mean?

Fred: Yes, Ella I mean.

Ella: How?

Fred: There are ways.

(SOUNDS HAVE CEASED)

Ella: They've gone quiet.

Fred: They're waiting now.

Ella: It's time, then.

Fred: It's time.

Ella: Goodbye, Mr er...

Fred: He's dead, Ella.

Ella: I know, Fred.

THE END

Namibia

The hyena's howl pierces cold hard dark.
Red tendrils begin to clutch blue dawn.
A predictable sun climbs high above.
The African sky stretches forever.
A land on the edge of infinity.

Purple mountains float on ghostly grass.
Springbok jets from pale whiteness.
Desert dunes, maroon with blue shades,
Rise steep pyramids from sable sand.
On rocks, a timeless leopard creeps, alone.

The palpable heat sucks air
From grains on the desert floor.
A Herero farmer drives his donkey cart.
Grey clouds of dust form foam in his wake.
The gravel road traces a mesmeric straight line.

Inland, thorny acacia trees jab and wind,
Creating a jaggy jungle of blue grey paper.
Dun necks of giraffes' poke pencils through.
Vulpine, the vulture waits on a black bough.
Dry leaves crack as, body tense, a cheetah pads.

The Atlantic beats a drum rhythm on the beach.
A bombing pelican dives, beak pouched.
Slithering, black fur seals groan, a heap on a spit.
Trilling quavers, dolphins dive on a page of water.
The sea mist curls caressing the Namib.

The African sky stretches forever.
The land on the edge of eternity.

A Moment in Time

His heart seemed to be stabbing his head in a steady rhythm and his breath was compressed in his chest. He could feel sweat forming under the prickly wool of his jersey. The afternoon sun was warm on his back, but he could smell the earth beneath him which was cold and moist with the decay of autumn.

He flattened his body further then wriggled a little forward. What was it they had said? "Keep still as a lizard and slide along the ground like a worm." He allowed himself a grim smile. He could sense his toes, cold despite the thick socks, cramping in his tight boots. All that training! This time it was for real. Would he be up to it? His skin felt taut as though it was a net laid out to dry, stretched over the bones of his body. Yes, he would do what he had to do. He was ready.

The shadow of a bird passed over his head and a whisk of wind touched his cheek. A pigeon cooed in the forest behind him. He knew those trees, silver skeletons marching across acres and acres of land until they reached dark pools. They were broken only by the gashes of grit they called roads, like the one down there on the other side of the hill. This was the way they would come.

He allowed himself to lift his head a little and rake the vast sky with his eyes. A skein of geese was flying from south of the river. Although they were high above he could hear their honking, deep and guttural like the shouted orders he heard from the house below. Thank God he had not heard the busy drone of an aircraft for a long time. They must have finished training for today.

"Lie still, merge with the scenery." That's what they had said. "This is your first mission. Make it a good one. Wait for the signal."

He tried to keep his mind occupied by sketching his memorised map of the little town. Why had they chosen this town for goodness sake? Well, the strategic position of the river, he supposed. If he strained his ears, he could hear the gush of the falls rushing over the rocks, supposed to be the biggest in Europe. But he couldn't believe that. The water had velocity, right enough, but no chasms into which to throw its spray; not like the glens of home. This country had no high hills, only endless birch trees. But he must admit that the high curve of the medieval bridge was impressive. There was no danger of not hearing a vehicle rumbling over those cobbles.

They described the town as a little Venice. Pathetic really. It was only a collection of houses arranged - as one would a child's toy village – around one of those onion topped churches. The streets crossed a series of rills and ditches. These were bridged by large stones. To the right of the road, after it came over the big bridge just below the church, was a 'duck pond'. Well, the buildings had some rustic charm, those wooden dachas with the fading gold of chrysanthemums and orange pumpkins at their feet, but not exactly Renaissance splendour.

The cries of children reached him. They must be playing a game of ball on the green. Poor little sods! He could imagine the life that was taking place in the town. The parents, slow-eyed, would be going about their business holding their thoughts to themselves, curiosity blunted by years of oppression, buying the necessities of rural life at the ironmongers and the grocery store. A few old ladies and soldiers would be in the smoke-filled teashop, warming their hands on glasses of amber liquid. Had it always been like this? Yet more poor sods! All those foreigners!

Just a little way up this hill on a path out of the village was the graveyard. People would pass when they could, clutching bunches of flowers from their gardens. There were so many grey stones for such a small place, lonely sad monuments. Everywhere here was the same. Earth to earth! Those who have served their country shall inherit the earth, or was it 'enter the kingdom of heaven'? He felt a gob of emotion in his stomach. Oh God! He was beginning to cry. He was going mad. It must be all this waiting. Action, action that would be the answer! No signal yet, but he must do something.

Tense and heavy, he slithered forward and parted the bronze fronds of bracken. He had a clear view of the large house on the edge of the town opposite the duck pond. Some windows were open and he thought he could hear the bell-call of a telephone and the tapping of a typewriter. But the voices were muted. The red flag with the searing black swastika swung out in a sudden gust but then drooped limp from its pole. His fingers curled round the hard metal ball. Yes, the trajectory was perfect.

A sudden screaming sent electric shocks to his spine. It took him a moment to realise that this was an animal noise from a mule in a faraway field who was braying in fright or indignation. These damned animals! He couldn't get used to them. Oh hell! Must he remember?

An image kept coming to him of the young woman. Even in her ravaged state, her beauty was apparent. Her dark glistening hair was hanging tangled and matted. Those big, soulful eyes were clouded with pain and her lips dry and scorched. Those brutes! Pigs! Hot anger welled inside him.

It happened so quickly, he found it difficult to replay it later in his head. The shrill rattle of a pheasant came from the forest—the signal! A large man in uniform emerged from the building, shouting to someone within,

"Sie kommen gleich!"

He heard the sound of a claxon. A black Mercedes appeared on the other side and bumped its way over the cobbles. He could see it was full of German officers. He didn't really remember lobbing the grenade like a stone thrown into the loch at home but there was a sudden explosion of fire and slowly, very slowly, as if in slow motion, like a whale turning, the car overturned and slid off the road, coming to rest in the duck pond.

"Cut, cut! It's a take!"

The director's megaphone seemed to be pointing at him like a Sten-gun.

I Prigioni – The Prisoners

Based on the statues by Michaelangelo in the Academia, Florence

A marble sinew flexes in an agony of stone.
A large foot grips cold white ice,
Climbs and reaches; climbs and reaches.
His profile screams a silent plea.

The body strains, alive but dead,
Curved round a rock of pure Ferrara.
A cave of infinite hardness captures
An eternal form of strength and beauty.

He scrabbles up the smooth surface,
Scratching invisible mortar with exquisite nails.
In marble bondage, see him struggle,
Power in his pain, the image of oppression.

The oeuvre unfinished, reason unknown.
A tomb embellishment for a Pope
Who needs a slave in stone to celebrate his death?
Is reason relevant in Art?

And who might he embody, this locked man?
The Renaissance victim of a politic plot,
A medieval angel slipping to Perdition,
Roman Christian for the lions, Holocaust Jew?

Is this a tortured soul imprisoned in his mind?
In his desperation, the shape of Death,
The battle of darkness in brilliant white?

Or has he found the final strength to climb,
To clamber towards that last window to the sublime?

Waiting

"The wee raj, the wee raj! I hate him! I hate him!" Her small round face creased into a worried grimace as her lips silently chanted the mantra. The hard, wooden bench cut a cleft into her buttocks under the thin material of her new charity trousers as she shifted her weight from right to left; crossed and uncrossed her legs. The fingers of one hand clenched and unclenched as she waited. The other hand lay lifeless on her lap.

"Your dolly arm, cold lump of clay, couldn't cuddle a fish," he would say.

This was a double dig in her guts. He knew she had only ever had one job and that was in a fish factory.

"Oh, sometimes it suited him fine with the Welfare, my dead hand," she thought.

She watched unseeing as the black-gowned figures rushed to-and-fro in the huge marble hall and huddles of desperate nicotine-stained, drug-shaking individuals pressed past the officials and through the big doors. She waited until the nearest door finally closed with a clang.

She heard the official sing out, "Court rise!"

She could see him now, flanked by the Court police, climbing the stairs from the cells and taking his place in the dock; a wee dark-jowled man with a jaunty step, taking his position with a kind of pride. She shut her eyes. She could feel his animal power on her skin so that her own flesh began to rise to the smell of him. He had told her so often she was a nothing, an indecent blob on the pavement, that she almost believed him. But, deep within her, she knew that, despite his bluster and cruel words, he needed her as much as she needed him. In Court One, just now, he would plead, "Not Guilty", and whatever happened thereafter, somehow it would be her fault.

He was an angry man. He had the right. Life was the "raj" for them both. He was a hard man and a hard love, but he was her only love, the man she had found in the hostel. She arranged her nylon-coated legs into a still, parallel juxtaposition, and placed the prosthetic fingers of one hand in warm pink ones of her other hand on her lap and waited.

Indian Impressions

Tossed rose petals form a pool of blood on cold grey stone.
A supercilious camel snorts. A harness jingles.
A curlicue cornet cracks the heavy curtain of heat
Which drapes the courtyard where the elephants,
Painted and patterned in purple coats, bow patient
Under the royal mahouts' dominance.

A room, gaudy with gilt, saffron, lapis lazuli and carmen,
Strewn with soft carpets, was sanctum to the prince.
Outside on the roof garden, arranged red plush seats
Await the guests. Below them, they see the city,
A seething mass of burning stars, while a man dances
Under a burden of pots, a twisted smile on his hermaphrodite face.

The narrow street smells of dust, jasmine, dung and sewers.
A naked boy pirouettes in a puddle while his sister extends a grubby hand
In her dance to the rhythmic beating of copper pots on doorsteps.
Men kneel, legs crossed in concentration, while others scream gossip
Across dark alleyways and ancient wooden lintels, draped with
Coloured scarves in silks maroon, gold, opal, garnet dark as blood.
Delicate maroon flowers etched on white embellish the walls.

The marble glistens, a deathly pallor while the rising sun
Catches a ruby in its ray, a sparkling drop of blood.
A group of masons cackle welcome to their ancient craft.
Far below, the river flows. A grey heron waits, a watchful predator,
While the brown waters toss and tumble a crimson garland of death.

The taxis honk a teeming mass and the bullock ambles to the dry grass
    verge.
A beggar hops one-footed to join a group of men haggling in their game.

They crouch by the roadside, spitting betel nut blood-stains on the
   pavement.
A child, mouth red rimmed, gives a sudden scream as the monkey steals
   his sweets.
The cobra with evil eyes and darting tongue rises to twist and turn
Like a wreath of smoke to the thin whine of the owner's flute.

The grey walls of the fort hang like folds of material pinned to the blue
   sky.
A raptor dips and dives in the clouds far above.

The Sweet Dreams of Miss MacCaffie

It was terrible, absolutely awful! Miss MacCaffie drew up her diminutive frame, pulling taut her soldier-straight shoulders, the product of strict deportment classes at a private girls' school. She tightened her thin blue-veined hands into fists which pushed down onto the mahogany frame of the large bay window overlooking a quiet Edinburgh street on a dull autumn afternoon. Her gaze was fixed on the cars which littered the road. Cars of every type and size were parked at all angles. Some even overlapped the pavement. Bumpers nudged bumpers like a bizarre dodgem ride where the music had stopped, freezing the vehicles in mid-motion. A gigantic bull of a green van appeared to be mounting a red mini!

Utter chaos! Totally unacceptable! Those Rugger Buggers! No, she could not even allow herself to think that word! She quickly substituted Rugger Louts. The strongest words Daddy had ever used were Hells Bells! Emotion consumed her. She was conscious that her breathing was becoming shallow and quick and her heart was beating like a panting dog in her chest. Breathe deeply, Dorothea. Calm yourself and think. There must be a solution even if your letters to the council produced no helpful response. Concentrate! Her legs felt weak so she sought refuge in her large winged chintz chair with its lace embroidered antimacassar and set about addressing the problem.

Looking around the drawing room of her flat, she felt comforted. The solid wood of the substantial writing desk, the bookcase filled with leather bound volumes in faded colours, the nest of delicate tables with scrollwork in gilt and ivory, inherited from an uncle who had lived in the Far East, the muted ticking of the grandmother clock, the burnished brass of the fire surround, the ornaments on the mantelpiece including the ebony elephant with knowing ivory eyes which had been a gap year present from her nephew. All cast a soothing spell of normality.

Dorothea MacCaffie liked to think that there was a solution to every problem. She was inordinately fond of completing crosswords and an avid reader of murder mysteries. It is beholden on me to find an answer, she thought. A lifetime spent in dusty libraries in a minor Government post had prepared her. Although for many years, she had embraced a quiet life, she remained a public spirited individual. While nowadays she very seldom extracted her modest Fiesta from its private parking space, the unfairness of not being able to do this because a large black Jaguar now blocked its exit rankled her soul. And what about that pleasant young lady on the second landing who was frequently to be seen struggling with shopping bags and a double-buggy? What if she had a medical emergency for one of the children and couldn't get her car out?

A distant roar reached her ears. One side must have scored! It was not that she did not entirely care for rugby as a sport. When Scotland won a game, her partisan heart was significantly cheered. Daddy had liked the game. Indeed, she believed he had contributed to the Stadium when it was built. What she could not abide was the selfishness, the deterioration of behaviour among the supporters. Once, at lunchtime in Princes Street, she had seen them proceeding towards the West End; a great sea of shouting, seething, tartan-kilted, woolly-bunnet-wearing, lion rampant flag-waving fans interspersed with other groups of small swarthy red hatted equally vocal persons, surging and swamping all the shoppers on the pavement. She had felt quite unsteady and had resorted to entering a store she did not like to frequent to seek a restorative cup of tea.

Of course, she was lucky not to live in the immediate vicinity of Murrayfield stadium, unlike her friend Hilda. With horror, she recalled Hilda's accounts of wild and raucous behaviour at bus stops, the piercing squeals of bagpipes badly played and chanting of Scots songs in ill matched voices. She had described dreadful debris, cans, bottles, piles of plastic and paper rubbish, items of clothing and other things quite unmentionable in polite society, all discarded by the wave of bodies. The noise and smell were disturbing in such a genteel neighbourhood.

At first, Hilda had merely hinted that she had a shocking story to reveal but, eventually, over a cup of tea and currant scones, she had whispered the ugly details which Dorothea now allowed her mind to reconstruct.

Hilda was a great one for gardening, and looked after the communal garden behind her flat, tucked away from the main thoroughfare and rugby route which fronted the tenements. It must have been Spring because Hilda had been engaged in planting the bed behind the privet hedge. She had just "watered in" the seedlings and was standing hose in hand considering her work when she was interrupted by the loud and far from dulcet voices of three males. They had entered the square and were on the other side of the hedge. This was unexpected since Scotland had lost and Hilda thought that the crowd disgorged from the Stadium would have dispersed. The men were arguing above the sound of clinking glass. One of them said, "Weel Ah'm dessperate!" and there before Hilda's eyes something pink poked through the hedge and a jet of foul smelling yellow liquid splashed onto the pale green shoots. Despite her disgust and stupefaction, Hilda had reacted as only a refined and sensible lady could. She discharged a gush of water from her well-directed hose. Hilda had recounted that she heard a yell of discomfiture before retreating hurriedly indoors. A small smile formed on Dorothea's thin lips.

Her thoughts were disturbed by the tinkling of the doorbell. When she opened the door, she found a small boy on the threshold. He was slightly dishevelled, his jeans grubby at the ends, socks in rolls above black trainers which were severely scuffed and a sweatshirt which was a little too small for him. He kept pulling this down as he shifted from one foot to the other. Thick ginger hair fell in a fringe over the eyes in his freckled face which he now raised in an earnest gaze.

"Well what do you want, Sandy Scott? What are you doing here?"

As she spoke, she noticed a thin black line like a crooked moustache around the corners of his mouth.

"What have you been eating, Sandy?" She maintained a severe tone but actually she had rather a soft spot for the boy who lived on the top floor.

Of course, he was a scallywag! There was the time she had been coming down the worn stone stairs and her foot had caught on that skateboard thing he had left in the hall. She had twirled round and only managed to stop herself launching into flight by clutching the bannister. She was giddy and angry until she remembered a similar incident with a go-kart pictured in the Beano. That had caused her brother and her to laugh so much they developed hiccups, so she forgave Sandy his carelessness. He wasn't a bad boy, usually polite and he looked very nice in his school uniform. Then there was that other time when he had found a stray puppy and used a piece of string to make a collar and lead for it. She happened to be coming back from the shops and he had taken her hand and asked her to be the one to report it to the RSSPCA and the police. No, he was really quite a likeable wee boy but it did not pay to be too tolerant.

"Aw Miss MacCaffie, me and my pal, Ross, we're going to a Halloween party, see, so we were just practicing with the treacle scones."

"Well, Sandy, I advise you to use your handkerchief if you have such a thing. And what is the reason I have the pleasure of a visit?" She kept the door firmly half open.

Sandy had rehearsed his speech and it came out in a tumble of words.

"Please, Miss, have you any wee jobs which need doing for which ah could be re-comp-ens-ed?" He stumbled over the last word which he had clearly just learned. She found his wee grin of pride rather engaging.

"So, Sandy, you are seeking money for services rendered. And what charity, if I may ask, will be the recipient of the aforesaid monies?"

He looked puzzled.

"Are you perhaps collecting for the Boy Scouts?"

"Aw, Miss MacCaffie, it's no for them. It's so I can get a new bike! Steven says the old one's a write-off." He added in a confidential tone, "Ah wiz doing wheelies and jumps and now it's totally buckled."

Miss MacCaffie knew that Steven was Sandy's mother's partner who had moved in just two years previously. She felt a pang of sadness for Sandy who had lived alone with his mother for most of his life.

"Can Steven and your mother not help you?"

"They said Ah have to learn the value of things and save up and then they might match fund it, but Ah wiznae sure what that meant. But it's too much!" he said sadly.

"Sandy, does your mother know you are here?" she asked.

He flushed. "Well, she said it would be good if ah earned extra pocket money and she wanted me out of the house. She said she and Steven needed some quality down-time. Ah'm allowed to talk to strangers Ah know, like you Miss Maccaffie," he added confidently and beamed up at her.

She shook her head. "Oh, Sandy, you better come in then. I suppose I've a pair of shoes you could clean and the fire-irons need brightening."

Half an hour later, she surveyed her kitchen floor, covered with newspapers, a patchwork of shiny black pools on the surface of the paper and dirty rags strewn hither and thither. The wee boy's face wore a similar patchwork as black marks on cheeks, chin and nose had joined the treacle. The eyes shone, and the mouth wore a triumphant smile.

"They look great, now, Miss."

She sighed inwardly. It was apparent that Sandy had never previously had the opportunity for this endeavour. Her sturdy brogues sat squarely in the middle, somewhat streaky and scarcely better of the polish and, while the tops of the poker and tongs gleamed, the bottoms were still dull white from the Brasso pads which had been generously applied. Sandy's hands were so black they reminded her of the chimney sweeps she had observed as a child. She ushered him into the bathroom and, as she witnessed his joyful lathering of her Pears original and the dark rim forming on the white porcelain, she shuddered at the thought of what Jeannie, her cleaner, would say.

"Well I suppose the labourer must be rewarded for his pains."

She extracted a pound coin from her purse but, seeing his downcast face, she replaced it with a two-pound coin and then, on a whim, added the first coin.

"Aw thank you, Miss MacCaffie, thank you very much."

"Just a minute, Sandy."

She opened a drawer and withdrew her precious poke of green sweets. "Just one Soor Ploom to suck on your way home. We can all do with some sweetness. Straight home now, Sandy. Those rugby people will be out on the street very soon!"

That night, Miss MacCaffie woke with a start from a rather disturbing dream. She had been situated in a bog which consisted of thick, syrupy black pools surrounded by round myrtle bushes which looked like shiny Christmas balls of a particularly vivid green. Suddenly, a group arrived wearing toggle hats, long scarves wound round their necks, a number sporting kilts, all chanting an indiscernible song. They proceeded to jump into the pools. She had seen one stick his fingers into the liquid and she heard the 'gloop' sound as he withdrew them. He had waved his blackened fingers in the air like a mime artist and then started to suck each one with a cry of delight. Then, she saw the others trying the same thing but their cries of laughter had turned to despair as they tried to pull themselves out and found they were stuck fast. As is the way of dreams, the whole scene became superimposed by the familiar face of a wee boy

115

with a treacle moustache, grinning mightily!

As the image faded, she found her old heart was beating rather too fast. Perhaps I should take another Aspirin, she thought? However, leaning back on her cool embroidered pillow, she reflected on the dream. She did believe that dreams could be informative and were nature's way of sorting the dross of the day. An idea came to her which caused her old heart to pump with creative excitement. The next day she would buy what she required.

On the day of the International, Dorothea MacCaffie stood at her long window and from her discreet position by the velvet curtains, observed the vehicles being deposited in the usual disarray. She switched on the radio and waited until the whistle had been blown and a garbling announcer could guarantee that the match was underway. Donning her dark raincoat with the hood and dragging her small shopping trolley with its load, she emerged from her tenement into the grey drizzle of a dreich afternoon. You could describe me as a veritable Hoodie, she chuckled.

The street was deserted. As she had predicted, everyone was inside watching the match or pursuing other activities. No human traffic, thank goodness. She was becoming dizzy with anticipation of her plan and had to lean briefly on the railings of a garden. Now to business, Dorothea. Sidling up to the driver's door of the nearest parked car she pretended to bend down as if she had a stitch in her side or was fastening her shoelace but was actually unzipping her shopping trolley and pulling out the tin, the top of which she had already loosened with a penny. It was a great pity, she thought, that tins were only sold in a regular size, probably too small for her total requirement, so she had taken the precaution of buying two. She had also been obliged to buy a full set of brushes due to the expensive way they were packaged nowadays.

With due care and attention, she applied the sticky sweet black paint to every door handle. Initially, she made several nervous quick glances in each direction but was soon absorbed in her task lulled by the hum and occasional distant roars from the Stadium. Rather like those people in Corstorphine, near the Zoo, you soon cease to hear the lions, she thought. She did have one minor fright when large Mr Ritchie from number ninety-four came lumbering along the road with his shopping bags, but she nipped behind a van, so he did not see her little figure.

She had completed one side and was about to embark on the other when a small voice startled her, and a wee figure appeared beside her from between the parked cars.

"What are you doing, Miss MacCaffie? Ah've been watching you and you seem awfully busy. Are you painting? Ah like painting. Ah could help you. Prapps ah could earn more for my fund?" He looked hopeful.

"Oh, good afternoon, Sandy. I am completing important covert business. I have good reason."

She pursed her lips and then realised that she had placed the open tin and brush at her feet on the pavement and that the gardening gloves which she had worn for protection were sticky and stained black. She took the offensive.

"Well er, Sandy, I could well ask what you are doing. Are you not watching the match?" This was rather unfair, but he seemed not to mind.

"Ach, Ah don't like contact sports, Miss. Ah'm good at putting and swinging." He demonstrated, swiping the air as though it was a monster. "Ah'm going to play golf when ah'm big," he stated with confidence.

She hoped he could be distracted. "Sandy, what were you doing crouching by the bonnet of that car?"

"Well, Miss, it's a BMW. They have silver signs. Some people collect them. Ah wiz jist looking."

Oh dear she had a sneaking suspicion that he was not just looking. However, in view of her own activities…?

"You said you're doing cov – something business, Miss. Like spies and stuff? Are you painting black stuff on to catch the baddies like finger printing and stuff?"

He must have seen this on television and now perhaps also a vision of a little old lady detective had come into his head. "Are you like Miss Marple?"

"Well, Sandy, I am on a secret mission for the public good." She felt this was an inspired suggestion. "Perhaps if you are very careful and don't tell anyone about it you could join me?" She was beginning to feel a little cold and weary.

He beamed, "Aw Miss MacCaffie you can trust me. Ah won't tell. Cross my heart—hope to die. What do Ah do?"

He was an enthusiastic if rather messy worker, yet they completed the task in half the time it would have taken her. He was also an excellent look-out, so they were able to conceal their activities from the few persons who ventured along the street.

Sometime later, having sent Sandy home with a sizeable donation in his pocket (immoral though she knew it was, she justified it as for the greater good) and a soor ploom in his mouth, she settled herself in her favourite chair by the windows with her china cup of tea on the little table beside her.

A great ache of tiredness possessed her fragile bones drawing her down into the cushions. The match must have gone into injury time, surely? She was convinced they were due out at least ten minutes ago. Time to walk back to their cars. Any time now. And then? A sticky end! Her lips twitched, shook and produced a little gurgle of giggles which grew and grew. Miss MacCaffie giggled and giggled and giggled.

She failed to see the first rather suave looking tall man literally stick his fob against the door of his four by four only to find his grip on the handle

118

slip in a greasy sweet grasp. She did not hear the furious swearing and loud protests, nor the beep of a police car summoned by the vehicle owners.

When Jeannie found Miss MacCaffie still sitting on her chintz chair, she knew at once that she had gone. She was to tell everyone later, "She was a real gentle wee lady; strict, mind, but she never had a bad thought in her life that one. And what was really fitting was that she had such a bonny smile on her face when I found her." However, Jeannie could never find an explanation for the open half empty tin of treacle which she discovered on the kitchen table and the black glutinous matted brushes in the sink.

About the Scottish Arts Club Short Story Competition

The Scottish Arts Club Short Story Competition was established in 2013 with Alexander McCall Smith as the chief judge. The competition is open to writers worldwide and for stories up to 2000 words on any theme. It carries a first prize of £1,000, second prize of £500 and third prize of £250.

The chief judge is assisted by a panel of experienced readers who review and debate all the stories in teams through successive rounds. Each story that makes it to the final round has been read and reviewed at least 45 times.

The Isobel Lodge Award is a special prize of £500 open to unpublished writers born, living or studying in Scotland who enter the Scottish Arts Club Short Story Competition.

The Scottish Arts Club presents one-year free membership of the Club to all the above award winners, provided they are not current or former members of the Scottish Arts Club.

The finalists, including the Isobel Lodge nominations, are invited to attend the annual Scottish Arts Club Story Awards Dinner. All finalists' stories and Isobel Lodge nominees will be included in a competition anthology published every few years, and the authors offered a page on the Story Awards website to promote their work.

For more information about the Scottish Arts Club Short Story Competition, the Isobel Lodge Award and the Edinburgh International Flash Fiction Award, please visit our website:

www.storyawards.org

About the Scottish Arts Club Charitable Trust

The Scottish Arts Club Charitable Trust was set up in 2014 to advance all forms of the creative arts in Scotland, to improve the accessibility of the creative arts to the public and to encourage and assist in the development of up-and-coming artists, exhibitors and performers. The Trust aims to expand opportunities for audiences across Scotland to see, use, and experience the arts in ways that can inspire, enhance knowledge, and even improve the quality of life.

The Trust supports a range of awards and prizes as well as exhibitions and concerts. We are developing partnerships and aim to raise funds to provide opportunities for artists, writers, musicians, photographers and others working in the arts as well as for publications, talks, and events.

The Scottish Arts Club Charitable Trust was founded by Members of the Scottish Arts Club. Whilst the Trust and Club are separate entities, The Scottish Arts Club has been the host to many of our events and the two work closely together to support The Trust's charitable aims.

The medium-term strategy of the Trust includes the development of the Scottish Arts Club Short Story Competition, the development of the Scottish Portrait Awards and promoting the work of writers, artists, composers and musicians.

Scottish Arts Club Charitable Trust is independent and relies totally on donations in order to continue its work. All Trustees and supporters give their time and experience on a voluntary, unpaid basis. All donations are gratefully received however small.

For more information please visit our website www.sacctrust.org. The Scottish Arts Club Charitable Trust is a registered charity in Scotland, charity number SC044753.

Acknowledgements

The Scottish Arts Club Charitable Trust would like to express gratitude to John Lodge and other family and friends of Isobel, whose generous contributions to Isobel's memorial fund enabled the establishment of the Isobel Lodge Award.

Further contributions to the Award Fund which is dedicated to promoting the work of unpublished writers born, living or studying in Scotland are very welcome and may be given through the Scottish Arts Club Charitable Trust.

Write to manager@sacctrust.org for more information.

This collection of Isobel's work was compiled by members of the Scottish Arts Club Writers Group including:

Sara Cameron McBean
Jeannette Davidson
Irene Gill
Linda Greig
Tom Gordon
George McGilvray Wilson
John McLeod
Andrew Mackie
Hilary Munro

Cover design and illustration by George McBean

29705396R00078

Printed in Poland
by Amazon Fulfillment
Poland Sp. z o.o., Wrocław